A FROZEN FIRE

For years Helen and Paul Eastwood's marriage had been a disastrous mockery. Paul was weak, vicious, blatantly unfaithful to her. But she was still his wife and some sense of duty made her stay with him. But now Mark Eliot had come into her life. What would happen to her sense of duty now?

Books you will enjoy
by CHARLOTTE LAMB

CRESCENDO

'If you let them, women will take you over completely,' was Gideon Firth's philosophy—a philosophy that had as a result ruined Marina's life. And yet she went on loving him. Could she hope that Gideon's heartless attitude would change—or would she, eventually, come to her senses?

NIGHT MUSIC

'I bought you, and what I buy stays bought, even if it proves to be worthless,' Steve Crawford had told Lisa. Was it any use her going on trying to convince him that all his ideas about her were wrong? Why didn't he just end with her and have done?

STORM CENTRE

In bitter circumstances, five years ago Lauren had divorced her husband Andreas—and that was the end of that. But now, after an accident, Andreas had lost his memory and was asking for her, under the impression that she was still his wife. For his mother's sake, Lauren was forced to go through with the deception and go back to him—but how long could she stand the situation?

SENSATION

Helen supposed she was reasonably content with her marriage-that-was-no-marriage to Drew Lincoln—after six years she was used to it—but what about Drew? Having kept studiously out of her way wherever possible, suddenly he was always there, disturbing, over-bearing, and—what? She couldn't possibly be finding him attractive after all this time, could she?

A FROZEN FIRE

BY

CHARLOTTE LAMB

MILLS & BOON LIMITED
LONDON W1

First published 1980

© Charlotte Lamb 1980
Australian copyright 1980

ISBN 0 263 09645 9

Set in Linotype Baskerville 11 on 12 pt.

Made and printed in Great Britain by
Richard Clay (The Chaucer Press) Ltd., Bungay, Suffolk

CHAPTER ONE

TORRENTIAL rain was slashing across the car windscreen, making it hard to see the road more than a few feet ahead. The sharp bends and stone walls made it necessary to advance at a cautious crawl. She did not want to crash or lose her way—this was inhospitable territory, judging by the empty, silent little hamlets she had passed so far, with few garages and fewer hotels.

Drawing up at a crossroads she consulted her map, biting her lower lip in concentration. On her right across drenched fields she could see ruined stone walls and on the map this seemed to be indicated. She sighed. What weather to get lost in!

At she peered through the curtain of rain she caught sight of a road sign further on and drove on to inspect it. 'Murthering Lane! How apt!' she muttered to herself, about to draw in her head again.

A startled cry burst from her lips as a horse leapt past the bonnet of her car from the other side of the road, its hooves neatly together, the great dark bulk passing rapidly. An incoherent string of angry words came from her. 'You stupid fool, you could have killed someone ...!' Her own voice floated through the rainy air and the rider turned his head briefly in recognition of her presence, apparently without alarm or apology. A wickedly audacious grin flashed over his face before he vanished into the misty distances of the fields on the other side of the lane.

She was astonished at how much of an impression that fleeting glimpse had left upon her mind, but then shock often confers briefly the ability to think and observe rapidly.

He had been a tough, lean man in an old brown tweed hacking jacket, the velvet collar damp with rain, his black hair flattened to his head giving him the look of a seal. He moved at one with his raw-boned mount, a figure of primitive fury, driving furiously into the face of the wind and rain. His features might have been startlingly handsome, but the stark impact of the weather had stripped all expression from him for that time, leaving a hard-featured mask beneath that wet black hair. Eyes of brilliant blue, a long, straight nose, a hard, arrogant jawline—so much she retained of his appearance, but the main impression had been left by that flashing, impudent smile which had made his blue eyes dance for one second, as though he were amused by having scared the life out of her.

When her shock receded, she took the turn over Hog's Back Bridge slowly, the empty brown sweep of the moors on her right hand, to find herself at the top of a cobbled hill which fell down steeply into the little town of Ryethorpe.

Helen had never been to Yorkshire before and her first impression of the place was not favourable. The sky moved overhead in a leaden torrent, black clouds riven to pour down rain in an unending sheet. On the edge of the moors here you saw the light filtering down through skeletal black branches, the grey sky stretching like taut canvas behind them, and in front of one the narrow grey streets of little houses, featureless and grim.

She drove slowly through the town, taking bearings as she went, and only took five minutes to find the little street Paul had described to her, pulling up in front of a grey stone house, a workman's cottage of the turn of the century, in a row of identical houses opening straight on to the steep pavement.

A curtain in the next house twitched and she glanced at it as she got out of the car. A moment later a young woman in brown slacks and a thick red sweater ran out, grimacing as rain sluiced down over her. 'Hi,' she called. 'You'll be Paul's wife?'

'Yes.' Typically, Paul had not mentioned his neighbours, but the friendliness of the smile she got was warming.

'He left a key with me in case you got here before he did. Come in and have a cup of tea. You'll want one after driving all the way from London.'

'Thanks—and I mean that. I'm parched!' Helen followed her gratefully into her house, wiping her feet on the thick mat. The sitting-room into which she followed the other woman was small, cosy and lit with an enormous fire, the flames leaping up the chimney back, their glow reflected on brass fire-tongs, polished wood and the somnolent face of a small child in an armchair, who barely turned her sleepy head to smile at Helen.

'Karen Santen,' the woman said, holding out a hand. 'This is Terry. We've just walked back up the town from the shops and she's dead on her feet.'

'My feet hurt,' the child sighed in a very adult

tone, and her mother grinned at Helen, face con-
spiratorial.

Karen had her daughter's brown curls, thicker
and more wiry, their rough short cap giving her
thin face the look of a cheerful boy. More or less
Helen's age, she had an accent that was distinctly
Yorkshire, her manner was easy and cheerful. 'I'll
get you that tea before your throat gives out on
you.'

Helen followed her into the tiny kitchen, looked
round with appreciation at the row of plants on the
tiled windowsill, their green tendrils climbing up
to give the grey rainy light a framed softness. Damp
clothes hung over a clothes horse in front of the
stove in the far recess. A laundry odour filled the
air.

'Barry works at Eliot's,' said Karen as she poured
the tea. 'Most of the men around here do ... biggest
employer in Ryethorpe.' She shrugged. 'Well, only
big one, we've no other industry worth the name.
Take away Eliot's and Ryethorpe would downright
starve.'

'Paul said that the town depended on the factory,' Helen nodded.

'He's getting you a job there, he said.'

'Nepotism,' said Helen, grinning.

'Why not? So long as you can do the job.'

Helen sat down and accepted her cup, sipped it
with a sigh of relief and pleasure. 'I needed that.'

'The pot's full,' said Karen, sitting down and
pushing a plate of homemade shortcake over towards her. 'Drink up and have another.'

'Luxury,' smiled Helen, obeying.

Karen flicked her a funny look and she tensed for whatever was coming. She recognised that expression. 'Paul's a charmer. Quite a husband you've got there. Good at his job, too, Barry says.'

She did not need to be told that Paul was good at his job. It was one which perfectly suited his nature. He had a charming, easy manner which made it hard for people to resist him when he chose to exert himself, and salesmanship had probably begun for him while he was in his cradle, selling himself to the cooing women who bent over his pram to exclaim over his golden-haired good looks and smile. He had been selling himself ever since, widening the field when he started work to sell the product he represented.

Karen took Helen's cup and refilled it. 'Are you hungry? I could cook something for you. No trouble ... I must start getting Barry's dinner soon.'

Helen sipped her tea, saying, politely, 'You're very kind. No, thank you, I'll get something later.'

'Paul told me about your mother,' Karen said later. 'That was bad luck just when you were moving.'

'Yes,' said Helen, pushing back a strand of fine silvery blonde hair, 'it was a shock.' She had grown used to accepting condolences, passing over the subject as quickly as possible. Her mother's death was too recent, her own grief too deep, to be discussed with strangers. She smiled at Karen. 'Does it ever stop raining?'

'Not often,' said Karen, then laughed and shook her head. 'Oh, it does, believe me, and on a fine day the moors are lovely. You can walk out on them on

a spring morning and never catch a glimpse of Ryethorpe. The town is down in the valley, you see,
right out of sight. From up there, facing the right
way, you could be in an empty land.'

'Sounds wonderful,' Helen said with a sigh
deeper than she meant.

'You'll miss London, though. We haven't much
in the way of shops, you know. No night life worth
mentioning.'

Helen gave her a brief cool glance. 'That suits
me,' she said, then got up. 'Thanks for the tea. I
suppose I'd better go and look over my new home.
Knowing Paul, it probably needs quite a bit of
work right now.'

'Oh, men are always useless, aren't they?' Karen
agreed with tolerant amusement.

'Some more than others,' Helen said, already expecting to find a kitchen piled high with washing
up and a house looking as if the storm had hit it.
Paul never bothered with the day-to-day routine
which keeps a place tidy. He lived from hand to
mouth, from day to day, from minute to minute, his
nature that of the hedonist.

'He's a good-looker, your Paul,' Karen said admiringly. 'Charm, too, comes out of every pore. I'd
be scared having a man like that! My Barry may
not be Prince Charming but he wears well, if you
know what I mean.' She gave Helen a quick anxious
look. 'Oh, take no notice, just green with envy,
that's me.'

Helen smiled, accepting the key held out to her.
'I'm very grateful for the tea. Next time you and
Terry must have some tea with me.' She walked to
the door, smiling indulgently at the little girl who

was now fast asleep, her rosy cheeks like apples. 'Poor mite! She is tired.'

Stepping out into the rain, she shivered, waved and walked back to her own house. She heard Karen's door shut. Along the quiet street she felt the stirring of curtains, the eyes behind them, heads popping up like caterpillars in a cabbage patch.

In a community as small and isolated as this one, there would be considerable curiosity about newcomers, she thought dully. Especially since Paul, wherever he went, attracted gossip like hair attracted to a steel comb. Her heart was heavy as she opened the door and went into the house. Beneath Karen's kindhearted warmth the slight stirring of curiosity and concern had been obvious. Paul had only been here a few weeks and already Helen could feel the familiar atmosphere thickening around her.

Her mother's death could not have come at a worse time. She had had to stay in London, first to nurse her mother, and then afterwards to deal with the tangle of affairs such events always leave, while Paul went up to Yorkshire alone. He had given her his word, his smooth, handsome face earnest, but she had had such promises before and they meant nothing. Paul was always glib, easy with words and assurances, eager to be given trust and sullen when, having broken his faith, he was reproached.

She stood in the tiny hallway, inhaling the stuffy closed air of the house. There was a faint odour of dampness somewhere. She slowly walked through the ground floor, inspecting the furniture which had been brought here from their home in London. It had an uncared-for look, the patina of well-polished wood dulled, the surfaces littered with newspapers and paperbacks, full ash trays, opened letters. Ash filled the little grate.

Upstairs it was the same story. The unmade bed, the clothes which littered the floor, socks and ties, discarded shirts ... She closed her eyes and groaned as she looked at them.

Bringing in her own suitcases, she changed into sweater and jeans, slid an apron over them, and began to work. It was several hours before she halted, the house neat and shining, the fire lit in the grate and giving the room a homely look, the kitchen clean and cleared.

She sat down at the kitchen table, yawning, her head aching. Where on earth was he? Surely he had not forgotten she was coming today? She had rung him twice last night and got no reply, but he had left the key with Karen, so he must have remembered she was coming.

At eight o'clock she made herself some beans on toast and drank several cups of coffee. She listened to the radio, her nerves stretched. By ten it was clear that Paul was not coming. Banking up the fire, she sat beside it, brooding, her face pale and angry.

It was their third new beginning. Each time she allowed herself to hope. Each time he smashed it down with the careless selfishness of a child.

This time, she thought bitterly, I will leave him. This time I mean it.

Where was he? In this remote little Yorkshire town with few inhabitants and no nightclubs, no gambling clubs, no bright distractions, where could he be?

She could not sit still. Sick at heart and furious, she walked to and fro in the tidy little sitting-room, occasionally catching glimpses of herself in the mirror on the wall.

She could have forgiven his infidelities if she were ugly, but she knew perfectly well that she was not without a certain beauty of her own, her fine-drawn features a little too sensitive, a little too austere, their bone structure imposing a cold delicacy upon them which her silver-blonde hair emphasised.

Paul would never have married her if she had not been much admired in their circle. Before they became engaged, Helen had had several other admirers and the competition, she realised now, had spurred Paul on to an eagerness which had decreased rapidly once she was his wife.

He had swept her off her feet, his charm and warmth holding her, making all her other male friends somehow negligible. For a few months after their marriage it had been paradise. They had spent most of that time having fun together, dining and dancing, going to parties. Paul had been in his element, enjoying the envy of other men as he watched her shining beside him.

She would never really know when it ended for Paul. For her it had been the day she discovered that he was having an affair with one of her friends. That had been the first blow which began the destruction of their marriage. It had cracked, like a stone edifice, the gap between them widening daily.

There had been a terrible quarrel. Bitter words had been flung between them, accusations of frigidity and dullness from him, from her angry distaste at his selfish treatment of her friend. Afterwards, Paul had begged her to forgive him. They had moved and he had begun a new job. A new leaf, he had called it, and for a while Helen had hoped that he meant to try harder. Six months passed and she found he was seeing someone else again. That time she had said she would leave him. Paul begged, he wept, and her mother sided with him. 'No marriage is perfect, dear,' she had said.

Helen had wearily said she would try again. The pattern was already clear to her, but she still had hope. As Paul got older, surely he must learn some sense.

Her mother had been very fond of Paul. All her life she had longed for a son and she had taken Paul eagerly to her heart, she would forgive him anything. It was during her illness that Helen discovered that Paul was up to his old tricks. Coldly, she had faced him with it. This time he had got himself into a tangled mess from which he was struggling to extricate himself. The woman was married and Paul, it turned out, owed her husband money. Helen had to cope with all that. Humiliated, bitter, sick, she went through it all somehow, but afterwards she would have walked out if her mother had not been so ill. Over her mother's sickbed she and Paul came together again. He had got this job and left for Yorkshire, swearing good faith.

It was a good job. The firm of Eliots ran an electronic factory in the little town, employing a good number of people. Their products sold all over the world. Paul had a good work record—his personal life had not yet intruded there. He had been given the top job in the Sales Department, involving a certain amount of travelling around the world. Helen was under no illusions as to his eagerness to get the job. World travel would give him the opportunity to indulge his flirtations briefly out of her line of vision, but at least it might make life easier for her on her own doorstep. It galled her to have to pin her hopes to such a fragile and humiliating chance, but what else had she?

From the outside, no doubt, her marriage looked perfect. Paul was so handsome, his smile so ready and cheerful, his conversation so charming. One had to know him to see the shallow, sulky selfish little boy beneath that golden mask.

The clock on the mantelshelf struck midnight. The fire had sunk to a grey, chill ash. Helen got up, shivering, and began to turn out the lights. Outside a car door slammed and footsteps lurched over the pavement. A key fumbled in the lock. The front door banged open and Paul stumbled across the threshold.

She stood in the little hallway, facing him.

He swayed, pushing the door shut. His eyes surveyed her sullenly. 'Oh, you're here,' he said, his lower lip held between his teeth. She turned without speaking and he lunged at her, catching her arm in a vicelike hold. 'I spoke to you, you bitch!'

Helen looked at him with contempt. 'You're drunk.'

He tightened his fingers, making her wince. 'Who wouldn't be, coming back to a sour-faced cold little bitch like you? I couldn't have come at all if I was sober.'

Her eyes were expressionless. She watched the

flush deepen on his cheeks, the glitter of his pale blue eyes. 'My first night here,' she said, dropping the words like icicles. 'You might have made the effort.'

'Would it do me any good?' he asked thickly, coming closer. The smell of whisky hung around him in fumes which made her turn her head away, her nose quivering with disgust. 'Look at me when I talk to you,' he growled.

She slowly looked at him, the cool oval of her face pure and cold.

Paul's fingers slid up her arm, over her tightly held shoulder, to her white throat. 'One day I'll throttle you when you look at me as if I were a worm that had just crawled past your feet,' he muttered hoarsely, his fingers biting into her.

'Is this what you call a new start?' she asked icily, her manner unchanged by his threat.

He pushed her back against the wall and his slim body fell against her, crushing her. 'Kiss me, Helen,' he said in those thick tones. 'You're my wife, for God's sake ... don't I even get a kiss when we meet again after six weeks?'

She silently turned her head away without so much as a glance at him. He made a grunted sound of rage and buried his face in the white skin of her throat, his mouth hot. 'I hate the sight of you, you puritanic little virgin,' he muttered, his hands going to her waist, closing on it possessively.

Helen shivered, pushing at his wide shoulders.

'Let go of me!'

'Damn you,' he growled, flinging away. 'Get out of my sight before I lose my temper.

While he lurched into the sitting-room she went

up the stairs and into the small bedroom she had decided to use. She had not slept with Paul for more than a year. He had attempted during that time to wear her down, coaxing, begging, bullying, but she had been adamant. She could not find it within her to live with him as his wife while he continually went off with other women; her own pride and self-respect could not consent to it. The first time she had forgiven him and taken him back without reserve; the second time she could not do so.

She was in bed when he crashed into the room. She sat upright, her face tense. He was in a dangerous mood. She recognised it from other such occasions in the past. Drunk, Paul saw her as the prime cause of his weaknesses. He chose to believe that her coldness had brought about his falls from grace.

Now he lurched towards he, his face very flushed, the blue eyes hot. 'I'm tired of sleeping alone,' he muttered, staring at the delicate tracery of blue lace which spanned her breasts, his hungry gaze delving deep between the half-visual white globes.

Helen felt anger mounting to her brain, sending heat along her veins. 'When have you ever slept alone?' she asked him with a bitterness born of old jealousy and hurt.

His well-cut mouth thinned. He lurched forward, catching the fine loose hair which fell around her face. She struggled, pushing at his shoulders, but he pulled viciously at the hair trapped in his fist, turning her face so that his mouth could find hers, his mouth violent.

For a few seconds she was on the point of tears. Beneath her contempt and anger her love for him still smouldered smokily. It was not easy to kill love, Helen had found. Her lips quivered helplessly, beginning a response which brought his hands down from her hair to her body, eagerly caressing her. She shut her eyes and tears squeezed out beneath the lids. 'Oh, Paul,' she whispered in husky tones.

Then she pulled herself together. There was no point in allowing him to hurt her any more than he had already. She had realised months ago that Paul was a taker, someone who despised what he got easily, hurt without regret. She caught him off balance, whisking out of his arms and off the bed. He fell forward, muttering angrily, and she backed away. 'Either you get out of my room or I leave this house,' she said coldly.

He lay for a moment, unmoving, then he pushed himself up off the bed and without a word stumbled out of the room, the light glinting on his bright gold head as he slammed the door behind him.

She woke him in the morning with a cup of tea. Fully dressed, he sprawled across his bed, his face pale and cold. He blinked at her as she pulled aside the curtains. The rain had stopped during the night and the sky was a delicate blue fretted with clouds. She watched memory return to him, his face flushing. 'You'd better hurry,' she told him coolly. 'You have a quarter of an hour to eat breakfast and leave.'

When he came downstairs, clean-shaven and grim, he pushed his plate away with a grimace. 'I'm sorry, I'm not hungry.' He picked up his cup of strong black coffee and sipped it, watching her as she moved across the room. 'All right,' he said without inflection. 'I'm sorry about last night. I got drunk and behaved like a swine, I know.'

'Will you be home for dinner?' Helen asked without comment. From past experience to answer only resulted in a bitter quarrel.

The gold head lifted and he gave her an angry look. 'Can't you even acknowledge an apology?'

'I've heard so many,' she said indifferently. 'Forget it.'

The pale eyes lit with icy little flames. 'You never forget a thing, do you, Helen? Every one of my mistakes is graven on your iceberg of a heart for eternity.'

'There wouldn't be room,' she said sardonically.

The cup crashed into the saucer. 'Oh, to hell with you!' he snapped, stalking out.

She followed. 'And am I to cook a dinner for you tonight or not?'

'I'm working,' he snapped, his direct stare daring her to question it.

'I see,' she said.

'Do you? Do you really?' Paul spat the words out, his face set in anger.

She shrugged. 'As much as I care to see.'

'And we both know how much that is,' he sneered.

'The way I behave to you is entirely conditioned by the way you've behaved to me in the past,' she said.

'You've got a lot of elephant blood,' Paul jeered. 'You neither forget nor forgive and every little misdemeanour is punished, isn't it, Helen? I'll be paying for the rest of my life.'

Her eyes met his openly. 'There's a solution for both of us,' she said.

His jaw tightened. 'No,' he said flatly. 'You're my wife.' Then he turned and walked out, slamming the front door. She heard his car start and move off, then went into the kitchen and began to clear the room.

Helen went shopping that morning on foot, walking around the town, inspecting the shops with interest. They were not a very large collection, but there were several good grocers within easy walking distance and she found a butcher's shop which looked both clean and efficient. At least the vegetables in the greengrocer's shop looked fresh and appetising, the prices lower than those in London.

Although Paul earned a good salary, he spent a large part of it himself, and Helen had learnt to be thrifty in her housekeeping. It infuriated her to know that so much of his money went on drink and pleasure, but she would not argue with him over it. This time, she thought, she would insist on getting a job. Paul had made her stop work after marriage, but he just did not give her enough money to make ends meet.

Seeing a good antique shop on the other side of the main street, she paused at the kerb to wait for the traffic to clear long enough for her to dart across. A sleek blue limousine slowly eased past her, then jerked to a halt. The driver leaned across the passenger seat to wind down his window and she automatically stooped to look in at him, expecting him to ask for directions, a polite disclaimer on her lips.

Wicked blue eyes smiled at her. 'Hallo again! Sorry if I scared you stiff last night, but I wasn't expecting to see a soul out on the roads in that weather.'

A cold brightness invaded her green eyes as she recognised the man who had ridden across her path in the rain. 'Next time I should look before you leap,' she said tartly.

He laughed. 'I was in a hurry to get home.'

'You should never have gone out in that rain!'

He shrugged, lifting wide shoulders in a careless gesture. 'Ah, well, we do these things, don't we?' His eyes dropped to her basket of shopping. 'Can I give you a lift home with that?'

'No, thank you,' she said, her manner cooling. The last thing she wanted was to attract the interest of her neighbours by arriving home in a car as glamorous as this one.

He gave her a quick look from rather too perceptive blue eyes, then waved and drove away. A few moments later Helen crossed the road and stood, dreamily, looking at a row of Victorian dolls in pretty lace-trimmed gowns, their round china faces bland. Helen never had the money to spare for such trifles, but she hankered for one of them— as a child she remembered playing with two similar dolls belonging to a great-aunt. They had left a deep impression on her mind. The stiff, formal way in which they sat in their tiny chairs was deeply nostalgic to her.

'What are you pricing?' asked a deep voice, and she did not turn, knowing at once who it was, her slender body stiffening.

'The dolls,' she said lightly.

The dark reflection loomed beside her in the shop window, his head inches above her own.

'Pretty things,' he agreed. 'If you're going to buy one I should let me do the bargaining—old Samson knows I wouldn't particularly want one and he won't try to edge the price up for me.'

'I'm not going to buy,' she said flatly.

'Not seriously interested or just not able to afford one?' he asked her, and she turned her cool, quiet face towards him with her brows raised in hauteur.

'That's my business,' she said.

He gave her that wicked grin. 'Ouch, a brush-off!' The long brown hand had lifted her basket out of her grasp before she had notice of his intention. 'Come and have some lunch.'

'Certainly not,' she said coldly. 'Give me back my shopping.'

He held it out of the reach of her hand. 'They do a good lunch at the Swan—a little stolid but sound English cooking. Their roast beef is perfectly cooked and my niece swoons over their treacle pudding.'

'How old is she?' Helen asked, amused, despite herself. He had a teasing look in his blue eyes which was irritatingly enjoyable.

'Fourteen,' he said in lowered tones.

'That's a bad age to like treacle pudding,' she said solemnly. 'It will play havoc with her skin. They tend to get spots at that age.'

'Don't tell me you had any,' he returned, his eyes slowly travelling over her smooth, matt complexion. 'I refuse to believe it.'

'Hundreds,' she said, eyes amused.

'Then you must meet Patsy and assure her that all is not lost,' he said. 'It will take a lot off her mind. She seems convinced that she's doomed to be an ugly duckling all her life.'

Helen was sympathetic. 'Oh, she'll be a swan, when the right time comes,' she said.

The blue eyes audaciously surveyed her. 'A swan ... the perfect description!'

She felt her colour increase and alarm bells rang inside her head. Drawing away, she held out a hand. 'Can I have my basket, please?'

'Only when you've had lunch with me,' he said, lightly yet with a note of iron determination in his deep voice.

She met his eyes steadily. 'My husband wouldn't like that, I'm afraid.'

There was a little silence, as he looked at her with a wry smile. 'You should have mentioned the fellow earlier,' he said, almost as though reproaching her. He held out the basket, shrugging. 'Now you've ruined my day.'

Helen smiled, liking him even more because of the way he had taken her revelation. 'Sorry.' She moved off, glancing back over her shoulder. He still stood there, watching her, his lean body held casually yet with elegant assurance. He lifted a hand in salute and she smiled before she walked away rather quickly.

CHAPTER TWO

A FEW days later Helen awoke to the sound of rain slashing down the windows and groaned in disbelief. Would it rain here every day? Glancing at her alarm clock she saw that it was time to get up. Heaven knows what time Paul had come in last night. She had gone to bed at eleven and fallen asleep quite quickly, and she had never heard him come in, but then her sleep had been quite deep, the sleep of the physically exhausted. She had spent the last few days in working to give the little house a more homelike appearance. Paul might not be in often enough to care, but Helen did. She could not bear to have Karen visiting her to find the house bearing the cold, unloved look it had worn when she first arrived.

Reluctantly she got up, stretching, washed quickly and dressed in white cotton cords and a white ribbed sweater. Waiting in the kitchen for the kettle to boil, she watched the rain whipping across the small garden, filling an ancient rain barrel which stood outside, the staves green with age and moss. Her mind was throbbing with images of cosy, stuffy London. Why on earth had she left it to come up here to this desolate place?

The decision had, in effect, been her own. Paul had not been too eager to take this job, but Helen had seen the chance of a new life in a quiet country place as a frail hope for their marriage, hoping that away from the distractions and temptations of city life he might change.

She might have known better. Paul had somehow found a place where he could indulge his taste for high living and gaiety—there were always places for people like Paul.

She took him his tea and found him fast asleep, his head out of sight under the pillow, the sheets rumpled. When she called him he did not stir, so she shook his shoulder. His hand came out and caught her wrist, pulling her down across the bed. 'Paul, don't!' she said angrily, as he swivelled to bend over her.

He kissed her hard, his mouth bruising. As he lifted his head again there was a furious sparkle in his pale eyes. 'I'm sick of being in the doghouse,' he muttered. 'All I get from you is snide remarks and coldness. I'm human too, you know.'

'If you ever looked in a mirror you wouldn't be too sure about that,' she said coldly. 'You're beginning to get bags under your eyes and your skin looks pretty unhealthy. You can't go on drinking without it showing, you know.'

He bared his even white teeth. 'I drink to forget the polar weather I can expect when I get back here!'

'It's a vicious circle, then,' she shrugged. 'One day you'll have to admit that everything starts with you, Paul. While you go on blaming me we'll never have a chance.'

'Of course, you're perfect,' he sneered.

Her eyes were icy. 'Nobody is perfect, but I've been faithful to you, Paul, despite provocation.

How would you like it if I played the game according to your rules?'

There was a silence. Red came up under his skin. 'You just aren't human enough to risk it,' he said hoarsely. 'You're frigid, Helen.'

She surveyed him with a coolness which belied the anger beneath her calm. 'Don't be too sure about that,' she said, walking out.

While his breakfast cooked she put a match to the laid fire and sighed as smoke billowed out into the room. She sat beside it each evening, her feet burning but the draughts from the window turning her neck and back to blocks of ice. The memory of central heating was galling. Raindrops spat down the chimney, making the wood sizzle gloomily.

A large part of the money her mother had left her had been swallowed up in paying Paul's debts in London. He had sulkily protested over it, suggesting that they pay the debts gradually, but she had been determined to pay his creditors back at once. Somehow she had kept the worst of the situation from her dying mother who still retained great affection for Paul, a loving indulgence which Helen now saw as being part of the problem, since Paul had grown accustomed to the idea that he could do no wrong where women were concerned. His own mother had spoiled him hopelessly, then Helen's mother had taken up where Paul's mother had left off.

Moving back into the kitchen, she served Paul his breakfast and he gingerly ate some of it, thrusting the plate away after a few moments. He did not eat enough, she thought, eyeing him with irritated concern. His colour was distinctly grey this morning.

'I've got a headache,' he complained, giving her a childishly sulky look.

She dropped some soluble pills into water and pushed it towards him without a word. He gave her a brief look, his mouth set, then drank the solution rapidly.

He put down the glass and sat there, watching her. 'What did you mean by that last crack?' he asked.

She gave him a puzzled frown. 'What?'

'In the bedroom just now! Something about my not being sure of you,' he snapped.

Helen had entirely forgotten the conversation, but now she shrugged. 'It meant what I said. I don't want you taking it for granted, Paul, that I'm here for the duration as a doormat to put up with whatever you care to throw at me.'

'A doormat? You?' He laughed hollowly. 'You're as bendable as reinforced concrete, Helen, and about as loving!'

Her skin flushed. 'I'm not getting bogged down in any more arguments about who's responsible for what,' she said flatly.

'All right,' he shrugged. 'So what are you threatening? Tit for tat?'

She was weary of the endless circle of reproach, argument and temper. 'Oh, go to work, Paul,' she sighed. 'Forget it.'

He sat there for a moment, staring at her, then got up and walked to the door. 'Don't wait up for me,' he said, almost triumphantly, as he left.

'Oh, I won't,' she flung as the door closed.

Then she put her hands over her face, feeling her eyes hot under her palms, tears threatening to spill from under her closed lids. It was all so hopeless. Why was she still here, in his house, masquerading as his wife? Their marriage had been over a year ago and only bitterness remained between them. Self-respect had made her fling that vague threat at Paul, but she knew that her upbringing made it impossible for her to do more than threaten. She was not mentally equipped for an affair with another man.

Karen tapped at her door during the morning, grinning at her. 'Are you going into town?'

'Did you want a lift?'

Karen gave her a sighing smile. 'Oh, could you? I don't want to take Terry out in this rain, she's got a bad cold.'

'I'll drive you both down, then,' said Helen. 'If ever you want to leave her with me while you do some shopping or visit your mother, you know, I'd be delighted.' Her eyes were wistful as she spoke. In the first year of her marriage she had had a secret longing to have a child, but after Paul's first infidelity she had realised the folly and cruelty of bringing a child into the tangled web of their lives. Paul himself had suggested the idea during their first reconciliation, but she had been wary of committing herself then. Later she had been glad she had never got pregnant. It was bad enough for herself to be haunted by the spectre of a ruined marriage without having a child involved.

Karen beamed. 'You're an angel! I'll take you up on that some time, Helen, believe me.'

'I'd love that,' said Helen. 'I'll babysit for you any evening, you know.'

Karen gave her an odd look, a slight frown between her brows. 'Thank you,' she said with faint hesitation.

They drove down into the shopping area, parked and left Terry cosily tucked up under a rug in the back seat while they quickly did their shopping in a supermarket. When they got back she was still reading her comic and Karen rewarded her with a large rosy apple into which the little white teeth bit enthusiastically.

They had a coffee before lunch in Helen's house. The little girl played with a pile of serviette rings which Helen had found for her to play with, building skyscrapers with them and giggling as they fell down. Karen said vaguely, her eyes not quite meeting Helen's, 'You know, my husband has two evenings a week out with his friends. Any evening you're bored you could come round and watch television with me.'

'That would be fun,' said Helen, smiling, but beneath her smile lay pain, as she realised that already Karen was aware that Paul was unlikely to be home in the evenings. Gossip spread rapidly in a little place like this—it had taken some time before people found out that her marriage was not perfect during their years in London. Helen had never confided her problems to anyone, but she had slowly become aware of sympathetic looks, whispered comment, curious eyes, and her pride had taken quite a battering.

If she had not had too much self-respect she would have asked Karen if she knew where Paul went in the evenings. She suspected Karen knew far more than she did—perhaps she even knew the name of the woman Paul was seeing. That there

was one Helen was certain: there were infallible
signs which she had learnt to read. Of one thing she
was sure—the affair had not progressed very far.
Paul had made several attempts to make love to her
since she arrived and had he been deeply involved
with another woman Helen guessed he would not
have been so pressing.

That evening she was surprised when Paul came
into the house quite early, still sober, his eyes
guarded as she looked at him across the little sitting-
room.

'Eaten yet?' he asked her casually, his hands
thrust deep into his pockets.

She shook her head. Lately she had tended to eat
quick snacks, her appetite small. It was beginning
to show in her figure. She had never been less than
slim, but now she was aware of a fine-drawn aus-
terity about her own features, a fleshless lightness as
she walked. Her clothes were getting too loose. Lifting her green eyes to him, she asked, 'Would you
like me to get something for you? Haven't you
eaten? I could make an omelette and there's plenty
of salad.'

'I thought we might eat out.'

It was months since he had taken her out anywhere and her face reflected her wary reaction.

Paul's mouth thinned. 'I thought it would make
a change for you,' he said, his voice surly. 'But if
you prefer to stay in ...'

'No,' she said quickly, getting up. 'I would have
to change, though. It won't take long.'

'Wear something pretty,' he said roughly, and she
gave him a quick, searching look. What was behind

this change of mood? Was it just another flash in the pan?

She picked out a dress she knew Paul admired, the smooth dark lines of it clinging to her, moulding her body to a long, lithe line from breast to thigh, the skirts flaring as she walked. She brushed her silvery hair upward, giving her features a cool delicacy lit by misty green eyes.

'You look pretty,' said Paul as she joined him, staring at her.

'So do you,' she said, her smile slightly teasing, admiring the dark suit into which he had changed.

His pale eyes sharpened on her face. It was months since she had smiled at him naturally and they were both aware of it. She felt a tentative quivering inside herself. Maybe this time, she thought, and at once felt that familiar sinking inside herself as she heard her own thoughts. How often had she said that to herself?

'I thought we'd go to the Country Club,' he said, and she opened her eyes wide.

'I didn't know there was one!' Although, she thought, she might have known there was somewhere like that for Paul to go to each night, a civilised meeting place where he could drink and talk and impress people with his charm.

'It's quite a decent place,' he told her. 'They shoot and fish and play squash and tennis, and in the evenings there's a good bar and dining-room where you can dance.'

He steered her out into the car, climbed into the driving seat. Before he started the engine he said huskily, 'Shall we try to behave like civilised human beings to each other, Helen?'

'Please,' she said in a whisper.

His hands lay on the wheel, unmoving. She put one of her own over them, her fingers trembling.

Paul bent his bright golden head over her hand and kissed it where it lay. 'I love you, you know,' he said, his voice muffled. 'I know that sounds impossible to you, but I do, Helen.'

She lifted her hand to stroke his cheek, letting him kiss her palm as it moved over his mouth.

Then she sat back, removing her hand, and he started the car. They drove in a frail, tentative peace, the evening wearing that hushed calm which comes after prolonged rain, an exhausted tranquillity which covers all of nature. In their headlights they picked up a darting rabbit which vanished into a ditch beside the road. The low stone walls surrounding the drenched fields showed up black in the light.

They drove out towards the moors and turned off on a side road between low ploughed fields. Along a narrow lane they spun into a wide tree-fringed drive and emerged from the black shadows of the trees to park outside a low white building brilliantly lit within, the sound of music drifting out into the encroaching night.

The man who greeted them wore a black dinner jacket and bow tie, his manner curious as he eyed Helen with admiration. 'My wife,' Paul said casually, and Helen caught the quick, incredulous look she was given. 'Helen, this is Drew, the manager.'

Drew offered her a hand, his smile filled with the friendliness of the professional charmer. 'I'm very glad to meet you, Helen.' He gave Paul a look she recognised. 'You're a lucky man, Paul. You didn't tell us your wife was a raving beauty.'

Paul's hand closed over her naked elbow, his fingers possessive. 'I'm no fool,' he said lightly.

Drew's eyes held cynicism, amusement, the lingering trace of hidden scorn. 'Well, Helen, I hope we'll see a lot of you from now on.' He was a man in his forties, thin, fit, his brown hair carefully brushed over his forehead, his brown eyes shrewd.

He showed them to a table in a long, rather over-decorated room, the imitation baronial style amusing Helen as her eyes took in the fake medieval rafters, the reproduction antique weapons displayed on the walls, the rich red plush of the velvet upholstery. It was all too much, but it was comfortable, the lighting restful without being too dim, the small band playing on the dais making a pleasant but not too obtrusive noise.

Paul leaned back with a proprietorial gesture. 'Like it?' It was the sort of place he liked, as she was aware, so she nodded, smiling.

'It seems very comfortable.'

'It is,' he agreed eagerly. A few people seated nearby lifted their hands in greeting and he responded with his most charming smile. Helen felt them staring at her and guessed that they were asking themselves who she was. Paul was clearly already known here as an unattached man and for all she knew he had given her a reputation among his new friends. Drunk, he was inclined to make acid comments about her, as she had discovered in the past. It was not only to her face that he accused her of being frigid and unsympathetic. After his last affair she had been told by his weeping, furious girl-friend that Paul had described her as dull, saying, 'Why I married her I don't know, she bores me stiff.' She had winced inside as she listened and her anger with Paul had gained a new impetus.

Paul ordered champagne with a lordly sweep of his hand and she made no protest, although she thought wryly of the small shepherd's pie she had cooked for herself and which would still be uneaten in the oven, the crisp golden potato lid covering rich thick mince.

How often did Paul drink expensive wine with his evening meal while she sat at home eating thrifty, careful meals? He loved making gestures of that sort, spending freely while he was in company, yet denying her all but the minimum of housekeeping money. The money left from her mother's small legacy to her was safely put away in the bank. Helen suspected she might need it badly one day soon.

While she ate her meal, Paul was talking to her charmingly, smiling at her over the table. 'Why don't we have a holiday abroad this year, darling? We haven't been abroad together yet. I fancy Spain. What do you think?'

She lifted her green eyes thoughtfully. 'It would cost rather a lot.'

'There's your mother's money,' he said carelessly. 'What's the point of leaving it to moulder in a bank when we could put it to good use? Now don't say your mother wouldn't approve, because she would be delighted to think of us enjoying ourselves together in the sun.'

Yes, Helen thought, undoubtedly he was right. Her mother would not have hesitated for a second in wholeheartedly urging her to go to Spain with

Paul in the hope of building a sound marriage with him.

She looked at his handsome, clean-cut face and saw the telltale marks of weakness in the bone structure, the shallow light in the pale eyes, the selfishness in the curved sensual mouth. When he was not smiling his mouth grew thin and cold, an irritable twitch to the corner of it.

'Let's think about that later,' she said, returning to her meal. She did not want to spoil the evening by a quarrel with him over such a small thing.

A new arrival was causing some interest around them, she realised a moment later. The manager was leading a small party between the tables, his voice obsequious, while everyone was staring. Paul glanced round and Helen felt a peculiar vibration from him. A warning tension came into her muscles. Was this Paul's most recent woman?

She slowly turned her silvery head and across the room met a pair of unsmiling dark blue eyes, their narrowed inspection sending a frisson of surprise and shock down her back.

The black head inclined slightly in recognition of her, then the lean body moved to take a seat at the table. She was oddly distressed by the cold look she had received. There had been unhidden contempt in his face, ice in the blue eyes. What was wrong? she asked herself. Why had he looked at her like that?

She concentrated on her fruit salad while Paul talked in odd, quick sentences, his manner excited, as though he were enjoying himself in a new way. Helen surveyed him with a puzzled suspicion. He had altered since the arrival of the black-haired man and his party.

She gave their table another quick, secretive glance. The dark head was bent over the menu and she was able to observe without being observed. There were three others at the table—one a young man in a light blue suit and pretty floral shirt whose face still bore traces of adolescence, his eyes hazel, his hair black and curly. She guessed him to be in his early twenties, and obviously his partner was a girl of the same age, her short bronze curls carefully arranged around a heart-shaped face whose pink and white was doll-like.

The fourth member of the party was a girl with long, silky black hair, wide sapphire eyes and a shy, flushed face. While Helen was regarding her the girl suddenly looked across the room at her, and there was a peculiar brightness in the wide eyes as they looked at each other, making Helen feel strangely that the other was on the point of tears. Then the girl looked down at her menu and sat there like a mouse, her little fingers trembling as they held the tall stiff card between them.

Sensing Paul's eyes on her, Helen looked quickly at him before he had time to look away and disguise his expression, finding a hard wariness in his face.

He flushed and bent over his plate. Helen frowned and bit her lip. Surely to heaven Paul hadn't been flirting with that child? She was no more than twenty, possibly even nineteen, her eyes giving away her inexperience and innocence. A pretty girl, Helen thought, but so vulnerable. Surely Paul couldn't have, wouldn't have ... She broke off the thought, eyeing him with foreboding. Wouldn't he?

He was smiling again when their eyes met later, but she knew him too well to be taken in by the hard gloss of his sophistication. The smile was too careful, too posed.

He talked about his job lightly as they drank coffee and she listened with half an ear, still pondering on the peculiar coldness of the look she had received from the stranger she had met the day she arrived. There had been a secret pleasure in the friendliness of their second meeting. She had felt reluctant as she walked away from him. It had seemed natural to be with him, an odd intimacy between them from the first moment, as though ... She broke off her thoughts again, starting.

It would be dangerous even to admit the thought, as she had been on the point of doing, that they were old friends who understood each other very well in that first moment of meeting. She was in such a delicately balanced situation, a married woman who had not been a wife for a year, who felt always that her marriage was doomed and an end to it inevitable some day. She had been careful to avoid other men since her marriage began to break up, recognising the vulnerability she was bound to feel, seeing the danger of allowing any other relationship to grow up. Paul's infidelity could not excuse any infidelity, either mental or physical, of her own. Whatever Paul had done, she was still his wife and if he could not take their marriage vows seriously, she did and while she remained his wife she would continue to do so.

'Shall we dance?' Paul asked her, pushing away his coffee cup.

Brought back to him suddenly, she turned dazed green eyes on him, her face still pale with concern. 'Yes. Why not?' she murmured, rising.

They threaded their way through the tables and joined the other couples on the floor, moving around to the music, Paul's hand tight around her slim waist, his cheek against her hair.

'Did I tell you that you looked beautiful tonight?' he asked with a slight thickening in his voice, his hand tightening around her.

She smiled and turned her head to look at him. 'You mentioned it in passing.'

The pale eyes gazed into her own. 'I can't remember when you last looked this lovely,' he murmured, his lips lightly brushing her own.

'Why, thank you,' she smiled, accepting the kiss.

He put his cheek against hers and they circled in silence for a while, the bright gleam of their heads close together, hers lighter and finer than his, the pale threads of her hair shining like spun silver in the lowered lamplight. 'We have a lot going for us, Helen,' Paul whispered into her ear. 'I don't want to throw it all away.'

'Do you think I do?' she asked, the faintest trace of bitterness in her soft voice.

'No,' he said quickly, 'I know you don't. You've been patient until now, darling. Be patient a while longer. Give me a chance.'

I've given you dozens, she thought sadly, but aloud she said, 'I'm still your wife, Paul, if you want me.'

'If,' he said on a sharp breath. 'I love you—I told

you.' His eyes looked down at her, bright with urgency. 'And I want to show you how much I love you, darling.'

He had no need to expand on that, it was in the sensuous movements of his hand over her back, in the heated expression of his pale eyes.

She hesitated, though, unable to throw away the caution bitter experience had taught her. He had come to her like this before, passionate, filled with needing, and she had given herself to him freely, only to wake up like a lost child on a cold hillside, empty and abandoned again, with only the aching wounds of his cruelty to accompany her into grief. She had sworn then never to give in to him again, to keep her distance, protect herself.

'Helen,' he whispered pleadingly, 'don't turn away from me, love. I need you. You call yourself my wife, but you won't let me love you.'

The green eyes gave him a long, sad look. 'I need more than a few hours of pleasure in bed from you, Paul, don't you realise that yet? A marriage is more than making love. I want a man I can trust to be there when I need him, not just when he wants me for a little while.'

Paul's mouth thinned in that characteristic way, his eyes glinted angrily. 'Are you starting to reproach me again? Can't you ever forget my occasional slip?'

The music ended and she stepped out of his arms. As they walked back to the table he slid his hand around her waist and bent to whisper, 'Don't frown. I'm sorry.'

She gave him a wry look and a sigh. 'Paul, what am I to do with you?' Why had she ever thought of having a child, she asked herself, when she was already stuck with one who was five foot ten in his stockinged feet and worse than any two-year-old deprived of the sweet it desired?

Her parents had had a wonderful marriage, warm and close and caring, giving her an untarnished image of the love which could exist between a man and a woman, an image she still carried in her heart today, for all the blows Paul had aimed at her over the years of their marriage.

She saw some girls at a table close to theirs eyeing him with sighing adoration, and caught the quick, pleased look he threw them before he turned back to her. He was a man who needed the constant reflection of his own beauty in the eyes of the women he met, she thought, a shallow Narcissus, glowing only when he knew himself surrounded with those adoring eyes. Perhaps in a way it was partly her fault that their marriage had begun to break up— she had grown up too fast for him, her first blind, unwavering adoration changing into the too-demanding love of a woman for a man, while Paul still needed the doting flattery of a mother.

He was twenty-nine now. He had been a man when they had married and Helen had been a very young twenty-one, her experience slim, her mind unformed, her admiration for his looks and charm blinding her to his underlying lightness. Helen knew herself to have a serious nature. She took life seriously while Paul took it as a child takes a game.

She watched him drink some whisky and hoped he would not drink too much. The music had begun again, so she rose, putting out a hand. 'Shall we?'

He got up and followed her on to the floor, smiling as they passed the girls who were still gazing at him with starry eyes.

As they circled the floor a man walked over to them and tapped Paul on the shoulder lightly. 'Mind if I cut in?'

Helen gave him a startled look. Paul halted, looking at him with a fixed, polite smile. 'Be my guest,' he said lightly, his hands falling away from Helen.

The other man swung her into his arms. Stiffly she permitted it, her eyes curious as she looked over his shoulder to see her husband weaving his way through the tables to where the three companions of her partner sat watching them with curiously blank expressions.

'Doesn't your husband mind if you go out with men like Eastwood?' he asked suddenly in a low, terse voice. 'Or doesn't he know where you are tonight?'

She switched her eyes to his face, her brows lifting angrily and coldly. 'I beg your pardon?'

His blue eyes held a glittering contempt. 'What does the man have? Even the sanest women seem to be taken in by him!'

Helen was angry but oddly filled with cold amusement. He had no idea who she was, she realised, and she ought to tell him now before he said anything which could embarrass both of them later, but somehow she said instead, 'Do you work at Eliots?'

His straight mouth tightened. 'I'm Mark Eliot,' he said shortly.

The name rang an instant bell. She stared at him, remembering Paul describing the managing director to her with irritated pique. 'An arrogant, big-headed swine!' he had said. 'Thinks he knows it all. Lays down the law without leaving a loophole.' And she had thought: Oh, God, he doesn't sound like a man who would take much nonsense, and if Paul steps out of line he'll be for it. Now, looking at the hard, tough face, she felt her heart sink because it was obvious that Paul had already given himself a bad name to Eliot. Why? she wondered. How?

Her lashes lowered, flickering against her flushed skin. 'So you're the boss-man of Ryethorpe,' she said, remembering him riding into the face of wind and rain like a storm god, his strong body poised on the great horse without effort.

She should have known.

Instinct should have warned her. A premonition should have hit her at that moment. Instead, she had first been angry, then laughed, and when they met again she had been too interested in his teasing, wicked smile to wonder who he could be.

'You still haven't answered my question?' he asked coldly. 'Does your husband know you're here with Eastwood?'

Her lashes lifted and the misty green eyes stared at him, their colour mysterious against the fine silvery hair. 'Yes, he knows,' she said.

The dark brows above his eyes jerked together in a frown. 'He knows?' He probed the cool oval of her face, the blue eyes darkening. 'And does he know what sort of man Eastwood is? He's married, you know, to some unfortunate girl he's left behind in London.' His hard mouth lifted in an unpleasant sneer. 'She'd cramp his style if she was up here with him, no doubt.'

'If you feel like that about him, why do you employ him?' Helen snapped, then was aghast at herself for putting such a thought into his head. If Paul heard her he would be rightly furious with her.

Mark Eliot's lips indented, coldness in his face. 'He does his job supremely well,' he said with marked iciness. 'That unscrupulous charm of his works like a spell on the clients he deals with. The women fall like ninepins and the men think he's a hell of a feller.'

'I see,' she said scornfully. 'You use him ruthlessly for your own purposes but reserve the right to pass judgment on him as you like.'

His eyes narrowed. 'I should have known better than to be frank with a woman who's head over heels with a swine like Eastwood,' he said.

'You've no right to make snap judgments about people you barely know!' she threw back, her head lifted, the green eyes freezing.

'What sort of man is your husband?' he asked, his words like tiny chips of ice. 'Apart from being a blind fool?'

The music ended and she moved away from him. 'He's the man I married, Mr Eliot,' she said with wry double meaning. 'A man I swore to love, honour and obey.'

He laughed caustically. 'By having affairs with other men?'

She met his eyes levelly. 'I'm Helen Eastwood, Mr Eliot.'

A hard red colour swept up his face. His eyes darkened until they almost seemed black. His facial muscles grew tight with anger only just controlled.

'You might have told me!'

'You were enjoying yourself so much,' she said bitingly. 'It's such fun to stand on a pedestal and knock other people down, isn't it? We've only spoken to each other very briefly once before, yet you walked up and started insulting me without waiting to find out who I was or anything about me. You deserved what happened.'

He listened, his eyes on her cold face. 'You were having a peculiar fun of your own, I suspect. You could have told me at the start that you were his wife, but you deliberately let me think the wrong things.'

Helen lifted her chin defiantly, not answering.

His eyes narrowed to dark blue slits. 'Were you trying to find out just what your husband had been up to while you were in London?'

Helen turned away without answering, walking towards her own table, pretending not to see Paul waving a hand at her from the table where he now sat with Mark Eliot's party. A hand came up beneath her elbow and that curt voice said quickly, 'Do you want to make a scene? Everyone here knows me. There's enough gossip about your husband as it is, Mrs Eastwood. You can come over and have a social drink with us.'

'I'd rather die,' she said huskily.

The hand tightened, propelling her willy-nilly in the direction of his table. 'Don't be so melodramatic,' he said with infuriating amusement.

It maddened her to admit that he was right. She was behaving in a silly fashion. She had always prided herself on her self-control, but she knew she had lost it at this moment, angered by this stranger whom she had only met once or twice.

As they reached the table, Paul half rose, smiling. 'Well, you've introduced yourself to Helen, Mark, but Robby here is dying to meet her. Helen, this is Robby Eliot.' He grinned at the younger man who stood up to offer his hand, his eyes admiring.

She smiled at him. 'Are you Mr Eliot's brother?'

Robby grinned. 'For my sins!'

'For mine,' Mark Eliot said drily.

Helen ignored him, her eyes on his brother's face. 'There is a resemblance,' she said slowly, although the hard control and dynamism in the older brother was not repeated in the younger. Their colouring and good looks were similar, however.

Her eyes moved to the girl beside Robby Eliot, who was regarding her with distinct coolness. Mark Eliot said politely, 'Sara Compton, Helen,' he gave Helen a quick, impudent look meant to underline the fact that he was using her first name while she was deliberately using his surname.

Sara Compton gave Helen a brief nod. Thoughtfully, Helen smiled back, suspecting the girl's coolness to originate from Robby Eliot's admiration which was still obvious from the way he was staring.

'And this is my sister Joanne,' Mark Eliot went on, indicating the other girl.

Helen tensed. She shot Paul a quick look, half veiled by her lashes, but felt Mark Eliot observing her and looked quickly away again.

Joanne Eliot lifted over-bright eyes to Helen's face and briefly smiled, a smile which did not touch her eyes, a facial contortion which passed at once into sombre stillness. Helen felt her heart sink. This girl was unquestionably miserable, every line of her pale little face confessing it, and Helen could guess why Paul was looking so carefully in another direction, a fixed smile on his face.

She sat down in the chair Mark Eliot pulled out for her and, as he sat down beside her, their eyes met.

She looked away hurriedly from the cool probe of his stare. This man saw too much.

'Paul tells us you want a job,' Robby Eliot murmured, leaning over the table with a little smile.

'Yes,' Helen agreed, catching her husband's quick glance. They would need the double income, she thought wryly, especially if Paul intended to keep up this sort of life style.

'Come and see me on Monday at ten,' Mark Eliot ordered in the sort of voice which brooked no argument.

'What sort of work are you looking for?' Sara asked in a slow drawl. 'What can you do?' And her tone suggested that she doubted if Helen could do very much at all.

Helen smiled politely, pretending not to have picked up that deliberately insulting nuance. 'Vaguely secretarial, I suppose. I have shorthand and typing.'

The waiter arrived with the drinks. Mark Eliot stood up, extending a hand to Sara. 'Dance?'

Sara rose with a sensual little smile and drifted away with him across the floor, their bodies moving with long-accustomed ease. Helen found herself watching them. Over Sara's shoulder Mark Eliot glanced at her and Helen flushed, looking hurriedly away. Joanne sat with her hands clenched nervously in her lap staring at the flickering candle in the centre of the table. Poor child, Helen thought, watching her. What exactly had Paul been up to?

CHAPTER THREE

HELEN and Paul remained at the table with the Eliot party for a quarter of an hour. Conversation was strained, filled with undercurrents of which she was aware, and she was glad when Paul finally made an excuse to leave.

When they got back home Paul tried to kiss her, his hands roughly demanding, and she wriggled out of his arms. Slightly intoxicated now, he glared at her and she asked him coldly, 'What have you been doing with that Eliot child?'

His face showed sullen alarm. 'Eliot said something?'

'He had no need to say a word. It stood out a mile.'

Paul scowled. 'Is it my fault she lost her head over a kiss?'

Sick at heart, she turned away. 'She's a child, Paul! You had no business laying a finger on her.'

'She begged for it,' he muttered, his lower lip stuck out.

Helen winced. 'You must have given her encouragement. How could you be so cruel? Common sense should have warned you to leave her alone. She happens to be your boss's little sister, remember.'

'Eliot has no call to sneer,' he retorted. 'He has quite a reputation himself. Women chase him morning, noon and night, and he gets what he can out of them without ever being fool enough to marry one of them.' His eyes stabbed her furiously. 'That's what I should have done with you, taken you and left it at that. Instead I was fool enough to make it legal, and I've regretted it ever since.'

'Say the word and I'll pack now,' she flung back, facing him, her eyes chill. 'I should have gone long ago. This marriage is a living corpse!'

For a moment he seemed speechless, his mouth shaking, the hands at his sides clenched into fists. 'You've never loved me!'

'I did once,' she said sombrely. 'You made sure I stopped.'

'Your mother was prepared to forgive and forget. Why can't you?'

'My mother wasn't married to you,' Helen said in cold, flat tones. 'We've been through all this before, Paul. There's no future in discussing it. You have no intention of changing and I have no intention of putting up with a husband who constantly chases other women.'

He walked out without another word. Helen slowly went up to bed and fell asleep at some time in the early hours. Paul still had not returned by then. She imagined he had gone back to the club and winced at the thought. Mark Eliot might still be there. He would stare when Paul came back alone and that cool, quick brain of his would start working, would guess and probably guess shrewdly. He might very likely envisage the whole scene which had taken place between husband and wife before Paul flung off in a temper. Mark Eliot was *too* shrewd. Helen did not want him knowing so much about her and her marriage. For some reason the prospect of Mark Eliot comprehending the situation made her want to cry, but she had cried too much in the past. She would not cry tonight. Grimly she turned over and forced herself to think of other things.

Whatever Paul did that night, he was placatory next day, his mood sober, his eyes begging her to forgive him. Helen struggled to retain a cool temper; it would do no good to lose it. She spoke quietly to him whenever he spoke to her. She did not shout or remonstrate. She merely matched her mood to his, her face remotely civil.

During the next few days they managed to reach a balanced form of truce, neither wishing to enter one of those destructive, savage rows with which their marriage had been punctuated. Paul came home each night punctually and Helen sat opposite him at the dinner table, exchanging limited conversation which held no seeds of menace to their marriage. They talked like strangers most of the time, but it was a relief to both of them to do so, and Helen gradually began to hope that this armed neutrality between them might slowly pass into something less unreal. She was still prepared to make an effort to shape their marriage into a real bond. Was Paul?

His character was not entirely his own fault, she thought, watching as he read a newspaper one evening. His mother had ruined him from early childhood. Paul had been too beautiful as a child. He had grown up into too beautiful a man, his features still riveting beneath that gold cap of hair. Life had been too easy for him. It had showered gifts into his lap and now he expected those glittering

showers to continue for ever. He saw little beyond
the narrow circle of his own needs and desires. He
must have grown up with the words 'I want' on his
lips, always sure that his desire would be fully satisfied.

He had made a mistake when he married Helen.
He should have found himself a weaker wife, someone who would be too grateful that he married her
at all to protest if he strayed outside their marriage
bed. Many women would have turned a blind eye
to Paul's little adventures. Helen's own mother
might well have done so. She had often hinted as
much, urging Helen to forgive and forget, begging
her to make allowances.

Helen knew all that, but it made no difference.
Her own sense of self-preservation, her personal in-
tegrity as a human being, made it impossible for
her to pretend that it did not matter that Paul took
other women. It mattered. The love she had felt for
him had largely leaked away in vain regret, but the
pain, the jealousy, she had once suffered had left an
indelible impression on her. She would never trust
him again. Their marriage was finished and she
knew it, yet she still did not know what to do about
it.

Divorce was an obvious way out, yet she hesitated.
It was a high fence to take without long thought of
the consequences, and for the moment she knew
she was marking time, waiting, giving herself and
Paul time for the situation to become crystal clear.

On the Monday Paul glanced at her oddly across
the breakfast table. 'Going for that interview today?'

Helen nodded. Throughout the weekend the

prospect of seeing Mark Eliot again had been eating into her. She dreaded it. His sharp, clever eyes would probe deeply whenever he looked at her. He might ask some more of his shrewd questions and she would have to parry or evade the answers.

'I suppose we need the money,' Paul said reluctantly, his mouth twisting.

Helen glanced at him, purposely cool. 'You know we do.' They needed it solely and simply because Paul spent money like water. If she had the management of their budget they would live very comfortably on his quite generous salary, but Paul only gave her a small amount each week for housekeeping. She knew how much he earned and she knew how much he kept for himself. The difference made her angry, but she knew there was no point in saying anything.

Paul read her glance, however, and his eyes flashed angrily. 'There's the rest of your mother's money! What good is that doing in a bank?'

'I'm keeping that for a rainy day,' she said drily.

Paul glanced out of the window pointedly. Rain spilled copiously down the panes, streaming into the gutters with a rushing sound which was becoming painfully familiar to her here.

Helen gave him a brief smile. 'You know what I mean. We may need the money one day.'

'You mean you may,' he said, watching her.

She was preserving that money in case she left him and wanted to divorce him and he knew it. It lay between them in a steely silence. Helen shrugged.

'Hadn't you better leave for work? It's getting late.'

He stood up, carelessly, brightly handsome in an expensive suit and shirt, his clothes immaculate as always. Helen felt him hover beside her chair and turned her cheek as he bent. His lips brushed her skin.

Paul still hesitated. 'I got the impression Eliot fancied you,' he said suddenly. 'Watch him, Helen.'

She turned, eyes wide in surprise. 'You're joking!'

For a second or two he stared down into her face, his brows close together, then he gave an edged laugh. 'I must be,' he said with bitter emphasis, and walked out.

Helen dressed carefully for her interview, choosing a charcoal grey suit with a straight pencil skirt and tight-fitting little jacket, a fine white silk blouse beneath it. Her silver-blonde hair was swept up behind her head to reveal the long pale nape, giving her a cool patrician elegance which her features emphasised.

The secretary in Mark Eliot's outer office had a distracted look as she asked Helen to wait. 'He's seeing a representation from the union. He won't keep you long.'

Helen sat down, crossing her long legs, and the girl shot her a curious look. 'Are you applying for my job?'

Helen's brows lifted. Before she could answer the girl laughed. 'Oh, don't worry, I'm going anyway. I've got a job in London. I couldn't stand another month in this place—I'm bored stiff.'

'It does seem very quiet,' Helen agreed politely.

'Quiet? It's dead, and the corpses don't seem to notice!'

Helen laughed. 'What sort of job have you got to go to in London?'

'A big firm,' the girl replied. 'Better pay than here, though, and much shorter hours. I can't wait to get there.' She eyed Helen curiously again. 'You're a Londoner, aren't you?'

'Yes.' Helen made no effort to expand on that, her face calm.

'How can you stand it here?'

Helen shrugged, saying nothing, her smile purely automatic. The girl would have gone on asking questions, but suddenly the door opened and some men began trooping out with heavy tread, their faces aggressive and unsmiling. Mark Eliot glanced across the office at Helen. 'Come in,' he said brusquely.

She walked past him and heard him close his door. The office was large and light, the sky grey beyond the window, but it seemed no longer to be raining, there were clouds drifting away before a cool wind.

'Sit down, Mrs Eastwood,' Mark Eliot said behind her.

She sat and he walked round the desk and took his chair, facing her with his hands on his desk top.

'So,' he murmured. 'What are your qualifications again?'

She quietly gave him her previous experience, her typing and shorthand speeds, her knowledge of book-keeping and other office work.

While she spoke he leaned back watching her, his eyes narrowed thoughtfully, their gaze never lifting from her face.

'My secretary is leaving,' he said. 'Do you want her job?'

The question threw Helen. Although she had known the girl was going she had not somehow expected Mark Eliot to offer her the job and faced with the prospect of working with him she knew she did not want to see any more of him than she could help.

'I ...' Her stammer broke off under his watchful stare. What possible excuse could she offer for refusing what was obviously a very good job?

His dark brows lifted pointedly. 'Yes?'

Her colour rose. 'I suspect the job might prove rather too demanding for me, Mr Eliot,' she said in an attempt at calmness. 'I was expecting to be offered something less testing.'

He picked up a pencil and played with it, his eyes on his own hands. 'I'm quite sure you're more than capable of doing the work.'

'You haven't tested my speeds yet,' she pointed out.

His eyes lifted, a wry sarcasm in his face. 'That's a mere quibble. I'm sure you wouldn't lie, Mrs Eastwood. Your speeds sound very good to me. My present girl is hopeless at the job and I'll be glad to get rid of her. I'm afraid we do not get highly skilled secretaries growing on trees in Ryethorpe. I realise you would expect a London scale salary, and I think we can offer one.' He named a figure which took her breath away. Paul had warned her not to expect anything like the money she could earn in London, but apparently he had been wrong. Mark Eliot was prepared to pay well.

He threw the pencil across the desk and watched as it rolled back towards him. 'Well?'

She knew that Paul would be incredulous if she refused the job. If she did refuse it, Paul would demand to know her reasons, and she did not want him to suspect that one of them was a secret desire not to spend too much time in Mark Eliot's company.

While she waited, trying to summon the courage to refuse, the telephone rang. Mark Eliot picked it up. 'Hold the line,' he said abruptly, then glanced at her. 'Well?'

Somehow the cold, level question made it easier. She took a deep breath. 'Very well,' she said, and at once wished she had refused.

Their eyes met and she sensed that he was perfectly well aware of her feelings. 'I'll let you know the other conditions of employment,' he said flatly. 'You start next week. Good morning, Mrs Eastwood.'

For a second she did not understand, the dismissal had been too abrupt, too unexpected, then she found herself out of the chair and on the way to the door. Behind her, his voice spoke into the telephone and she closed the door without looking back at him.

The girl was bending over a long sheet of typed green figures. She glanced up curiously. 'No luck?'

'I start next Monday,' Helen said a trifle breathlessly. 'At least I think I do. Is he always that terse?'

The girl made a face at the closed door. 'He can be nice enough, but he can be a swine, too. He expects a lot for his money.'

'Don't we all?' Helen said drily.

The girl laughed. 'I'll show you round, if you like, if you've got time?'

'Please,' said Helen, glancing around the office with interest. She could hardly believe that she was to be working here every day from the following Monday. When she came for this interview she had somehow expected to get a very minor job, something she could combine easily with her housework, something which did not ask too much energy and time of her. She had the suspicion that what she had actually got might prove very demanding indeed.

'I'm Deirdre,' the girl told her, holding out a friendly hand, her brown eyes smiling.

'I'm Helen.'

For the next ten minutes she followed Deirdre around the office, listening to the rather brief explanation the girl gave, understanding why Mark Eliot was not sorry to see her go. Deirdre showed little real interest in the work and none at all in her own capacity to do it. She obviously regarded work as an annoying interruption in her private life. All that interested her was what she did outside the office.

It was, Helen decided, a relatively interesting job, largely consisting of the usual secretarial tasks, but it was varied enough to keep one interested if one was even faintly curious about life.

'The trouble is the people we get trooping in and out,' Deirdre complained. 'Union men, managers, salesmen, personnel people. They all go in to see Mr Eliot. Some days it's nothing but interruptions, but he still expects me to get the letters done and the filing kept up to date.'

As she spoke the door swung open and Paul

strolled into the room. Deirdre's eyes brightened. 'Hi, Paul,' she said with a beam.

His handsome face returned the smile automatically, the charming mask imposed for the few seconds it took, his eyes holding that personal intimacy he gave to every attractive female he met.

Then he looked at Helen and his face changed. 'Seen him yet?'

Deirdre answered for her. 'Not only seen him. She got the job—and good luck to her, she's welcome to him!'

Paul stiffened, his head sharply lifted, thrown back so that the sunlight glittered on his bright hair. 'Welcome to him?' He stared at Helen. 'Did he offer you the job here, in this office?'

'She's got my job,' said Deirdre, laughing.

Helen moved towards the door. She sensed the build-up of Paul's displeasure and did not want to discuss it in front of the other girl.

Deirdre's smile vanished as she began to catch the tension between the two of them. She eyed them curiously. As Helen passed Paul he caught her elbow to halt her and she looked at him, her face taut.

'You're going to be working for Eliot?' The words burst out of him harshly.

She pulled out of his grip and walked out of the door. Paul followed and caught up with her, wrenching her arm towards him.

'Not here, please!' she muttered.

His blue eyes were narrowed in a stare which made them glitter like snow crystals in sunlight. 'I don't want you working for him! Why did you accept the job?'

Bitingly she told him how much Mark Eliot had offered to pay her and saw his astonished face and then the struggle which began inside him. Paul was taken aback by the amount, tempted by it. He knew she could never get as much anywhere else.

'Why did he offer you so much?' he demanded.

'My qualifications impressed him.'

'I bet they did,' Paul said savagely, his eyes flicking from her smooth hair down her slender body. 'And I can guess what he's hoping to get for his money.'

'Don't judge everyone by your own standards!' Helen told him with a half-savage smile.

His mouth twisted coldly. 'No, of course, Eliot is above such ideas, I suppose. He wouldn't fancy you, would he?'

'He wants a secretary, nothing else!'

Paul laughed unpleasantly. 'I've a very shrewd idea what Eliot wants, thank you.' He bent towards her, violence in the flash of the blue eyes. 'And he isn't getting it from you!'

Helen stared at him. 'You don't know the first thing about me, do you, Paul?' She turned and walked away and Paul stood there, staring after her without moving.

When he got home that evening he was in a mood she recognised on sight. She had had time to think and she realised that if she took the job with Mark Eliot she was putting herself into an intolerable situation. Not only would Paul bitterly resent it, but she herself would be under considerable temptation the whole time. Mark Eliot was far too attractive and she was far too vulnerable.

She did not wait for Paul to launch the angry

attack she could sense was coming. 'I've decided I won't take the job,' she said flatly as he opened his mouth to speak.

Paul stared at her, visibly taken aback. She had taken the wind out of his sails and the aggression leaked out of him as he surveyed her. Calmly Helen turned and began to prepare the table for the evening meal.

Paul caught hold of her shoulders, whirled her to face him, staring down at her. 'He does fancy you, doesn't he?'

'I've no idea,' she lied.

'Do you fancy him?'

Her eyes held no expression. 'I'm rather off men, to be frank.'

He drew a long breath. 'You're not frank, Helen —you're brutal.' The blue eyes grew ugly. 'But you're my wife.' He bent and kissed her, hurting her mouth. Helen did not struggle. She merely stood there without responding or denying, passive, a cold victim.

Paul drew back his head, his face white. 'My God, you hate me, don't you?'

Helen did not answer. Their eyes held in silence for a long moment. Paul released her, shoving her away roughly as though he would like to hurt her far more than he had.

'Very well,' he said. 'Take the job with Eliot. We need the money, damn you. Just remember, keep him at a distance. You may have nothing to lose, but Eliot could lose a lot if he got involved in a scandal, and if I suspect he's playing around with you, believe me, there'll be a scandal. I'll break his neck!'

Helen doubted if Paul was capable of laying a finger on Mark Eliot. The man would be more likely to break Paul's neck if he tried. However, she shrugged coolly. 'I'm quite happy to look for a job elsewhere. I leave the decision to you.'

'You always do,' Paul said bitterly. 'Ever since we got married you've laid all the burden of the marriage on me, Helen.'

That was laughable, but she did not laugh. She looked at him in sombre realisation, her eyes almost pitying. He really believed it, that was the trouble. She was Paul's excuse. Whatever he did, he could say she forced him into it, it was all her fault. He was guiltless, a wronged innocent.

As he read her expression his face almost writhed; resentment, jealousy, misery in his eyes. 'You're made of stone, Helen—cold, unforgiving, above temptation. Why can't you be human, like the rest of us?'

Above temptation? Helen shivered. Was she really? Her eyes moved away from Paul, a shadow passing over them. She hoped to God she was, because if ever she had seen temptation it was Mark Eliot.

CHAPTER FOUR

Two days later Helen straightened from a kneeling position, having just polished the grate until it shone, putting a weary hand to her protesting back. She had been working in the house all day. What she needed, she thought, was some fresh air. Paul would not be home for an hour; she just had time for a short drive up to the moors. Finding an anorak, she let herself out of the front door and climbed into her car. The late afternoon was cool and clear, the skies washed bright after earlier rain, a few faint gleams of sunshine touching the windows of the grey little houses around her.

She drove out of the town, turning into the side road which led across the moors, her gaze on the dark, heather-covered swell of the land, the contours rolling smoothly against the sky. She found herself near the ruined abbey she had seen on her first day and drew up beside the road, staring at it across the fields. Murthering Lane, she remembered, smiling. She had failed to discover the reason for the name.

A rough footpath led, muddy and little-trodden, beside the low stone walls to the abbey.

Helen felt a sudden urge to investigate the place, but hesitated, realising that it was growing late. She ought to get back, she thought. For a moment she hesitated undecidedly, biting her lip, then she made up her mind with a little grimace. Why not?

She got out of the car and locked it, then took the footpath, her flat shoes slipping a little as she carefully made her way through the field. The abbey ruins were startlingly remote, their broken walls like jagged teeth sticking up from the rough grass, the Norman arches of window and doors outlined in smooth red brick which reminded her of Roman tiles. Some old churches had used reworked Roman remains and perhaps this one had been built on a Roman site. She paced around it, staring up through the roofless ruins at the darkening sky.

She had asked Karen about it and received little information. The other girl had shrugged. 'I think it was pulled down years ago. They say it's haunted.'

Helen had laughed. 'They always do!'

Karen's eyes had danced. 'I'm an ignoramus— don't ask me! I've never been near the place. I'm not much on history.'

The ground was soggy with rain, giving beneath her footfall. A few windswept little trees grew in the shelter of the walls, their leafless branches sweeping the stone with a scratching sound. It might be quite charming to have a picnic here in the summer, she thought, but at this time of year there was something both melancholy and awesome about the place. It held echoes of the past.

Suddenly she heard a sound and turned, eyes wide, to stare behind her into the rapidly falling twilight. A shape was suddenly outlined between the ruined walls, standing in an arch. Her heart leapt into her mouth and she gave a scream, moving back instinctively.

She was too taken aback to realise that a heap of stones lay behind her, and she fell heavily, her head striking against a jutting piece of stone.

Dazed, she lay unmoving for a moment. Her eyes saw red suns whirl before them. Pain stabbed between her brows.

Someone moved beside her and a hand touched the side of her face gently. She moaned, her lids flying upwards.

Recognising Mark Eliot she gave a gasp, her face burning with shame and irritation. Who had she expected to see? She felt a fool. Why on earth had she screamed like that? Her mind had been so preoccupied with images of the past that she had behaved like an idiot and in the presence of a man she distrusted!

'I tripped,' she mumbled, hoping that he would not realise that his arrival had precipitated the accident.

'So I saw,' he replied coolly, moving her head as though testing it for injury. Her long silvery hair spilled across his arm, freed from its amber comb in the fall. The wind blew strands of it across his mouth and he put up a hand to them slowly. He smelt of rain and grass, as if he had been riding in the rain. Helen saw moisture on his tweed hacking jacket. The material had that familiar smell, like the coat of a dog. The rough material of his sleeve brushed her face as he slid his hand under her head.

'You hit your head when you fell. Does it hurt?' His fingers felt their way across her nape experimentally.

Suddenly her mouth was dry and she angrily recognised the symptom. She shivered and his blue eyes sharpened.

'I'm fine,' she said in a husky voice, and struggled

to get up, to get away from his oppressive nearness.

He caught her as she swayed, her leg buckling under her weight. She made a sound between anger and pain, head bent.

'You've sprained your ankle, I think,' he said flatly. 'Can you stand?'

'Yes,' she lied, putting down her hurt foot and biting her lip.

He gave her a curious look, then knelt and rolled back her tight white cords, his long fingers feeling her ankle. 'It's swelling,' he said, 'but no bones broken. My horse is tied outside, I'll take you home.'

'My car is across the field,' she said. She was angry with herself for that brief experience of sexual attraction.

His body straightened beside her. She gave him a polite little smile which did not touch her eyes. 'I'm fine now, thank you.'

'That isn't true,' he said casually, his mouth curling in contempt. 'However, if you prefer to walk back to your car alone I shan't interfere. You'll be in great pain and you'll make the sprain much worse than it is before you get to your car, of course, but that's your business.'

Her colour rose and she turned away. The first step was agonising, but she made it. The second had her half fainting. She stifled the moan which rose to her lips and the next moment Mark Eliot had swept her up into his arms like a child, her head falling against his shoulder. He strode through the Norman archway and laid her on to the saddle. She sat up, clutching at it.

He led the horse across the field. The sky had

grown quite dark. A faint white glimmer in the east showed where the moon was rising, but clouds masked its shape. The wind flung bushes and trees into exaggerated shapes, rustling among them as if they were lace petticoats. From the copse on the left of them a barn owl suddenly flew on steadily beating wings towards the dark shapes of farm buildings a few fields away. The weird call it gave made Helen jump and he glanced at her ironically.

'An owl, that's all.'

'I know that,' she said, ruffled. What sort of idiot did he take her for?

'Who did you think I was?' he enquired coolly. 'A ghost? That scream you gave made me jump myself.'

'Anyone would be startled to see someone at such a place and time!' she snapped.

'I ride that way every day.'

'You must leave work early,' she said, giving him a sharp look. Was he the sort of boss who worked short hours and left his employees to do everything?

He gave her a comprehending smile, his teeth sharp and even. 'I work longer hours than anyone in my employ, don't worry. I start work while most of them are still in bed.'

'Early to bed, early to rise?' she mocked. 'And are you healthy, wealthy and wise, Mr Eliot?'

'I'm wealthy,' he said mockingly, in response, a sudden amusement in the blue eyes.

They reached the car and she handed him the ignition key. He unlocked both doors, then lifted her from her horse and sat her in the passenger seat. 'I can drive,' she said.

'Not on that foot,' he contradicted. 'It would be

too painful, and rather dangerous for other drivers.'

'What about your horse?'

He shrugged. 'Wait here.' He walked back to the waiting animal and deftly unsaddled him. She heard him open her boot and fling the saddle and bridle into it. A few moments later he had shut the horse into one of the adjoining fields and was climbing into the car beside her. He gave her a quick grin. 'There's always an answer to every problem,' he said. 'Don Googe is a friend of mine. He won't mind if I leave Brutus there for a night.'

'It's very good of you to take the trouble,' she said reluctantly.

His eyes mocked her. 'So it is,' he said. 'Why am I bothering? You're the most ungracious female I've ever met.'

She felt her skin flushing. 'I'm sorry.'

'That's all right, Mrs Eastwood,' he said coolly. 'You can't help it if you resent the fact that I'm aware that you're married to a complete swine.'

'That's enough!' she said sharply, sitting up.

Ignoring her, he went on in a brusque cold voice, 'And that you're sick and tired of your pretence of a marriage but can't bring yourself to get out of it.'

Ice penetrated her. 'Shut up!' she muttered in thick tones.

He started the car, the engine racing. 'I've finished,' he said. 'It had to be said.'

'You had no right to say it or even to think it. You don't know the first thing about my marriage.'

The car shot away down the road, his eyes on the sky. 'I've seen enough of Eastwood to have a pretty good idea of the sort of man he is—they aren't so unusual, you know. Plenty of men stay adolescents all their lives. Peter Pans who don't even want to grow up. Eastwood has the sort of looks which attract women like flies. He's traded on his looks all his life, I imagine.' He gave her a brief, oblique look. 'How long have you been married?'

'Three years.'

He nodded. 'How old are you?'

'Twenty-four.'

'And he's almost thirty,' he thought aloud. There was a silence. 'Were you in love with him?'

'I still am,' she lied.

He gave her a faint, wry smile. 'Yes?' And she knew as if he had denied it aloud that he was aware that she lied.

For a while there was silence between them as they came down into the town, hitting the first orange street lights, his speed rising as he shot down towards her street. The house had been part of the perks of the job—it had been an advantage to them, saving them the problem of finding somewhere to live.

He drew up outside her house and as he opened her door she said quickly, 'Please, let me walk in!' She could not bear to have the neighbours watching as he carried her.

He gave her a shrewd, comprehending glance and stood back. She made it to the front door with pain while he walked close beside her, watching to make sure she did not fall. She was trembling as she finally half fell into the house.

'You stupid little fool,' he muttered under his breath, his blue eyes caustic about her folly. His hands moved to catch her and she weakly abandoned herself to their hard strength as he lifted her.

She closed her eyes, the hall going round.

'Pride is a poor substitute for sense,' he said, carrying her up the stairs. 'Which room?'

'On the left,' she said. He pushed the door open and carried her into it, depositing her on the bed gently. He walked over and drew the curtains. Helen struggled over on one elbow to light a lamp quickly, and he threw her a curious, searching look.

'Thank you,' she said hurriedly. 'I won't keep you.'

'No, you won't,' he said in a hard voice. 'And I'm not going. I'll call the doctor and get you a cup of tea. You're white, Mrs Eastwood, and you look like someone who's going to pass out.'

'This is a small town,' she said wearily. 'Everyone here knows you. You can't stay here alone with me in my bedroom.'

His eyes were bright and mocking. 'Yes, your bedroom,' he said, glancing at the small single bed. 'Neat and nunlike.'

Scarlet flamed in her white cheeks. She drew a bitter breath. 'Will you please just go?'

'I'm beginning to wonder if Eastwood is the only one to blame,' he said, and her green eyes burned with hurt and anger.

Mark Eliot waited, watching her, as though anticipating some retort, but she felt it wiser to be silent.

He grimaced. 'No rising to it? Well, it leaves me to draw my own conclusions.'

'Wouldn't you do that anyway?'

'If you told me the truth I would believe you,' he said, his eyes searching her averted face.

'I refuse to discuss my marriage with you.'

He came over to the bed and her whole body tensed, her eyes flying to his face with alarm in their green depths. His mouth hardened.

'Don't look at me like that or you may precipitate the very thing you're most afraid of,' he said harshly.

Her face flushed deeply. 'Please just go ...'

He sat down on the edge of the bed and pulled down the zip of her anorak. 'Trust me, Helen,' he said more calmly.

Her hand had risen to push his away, but now it dropped. She slowly nodded, surprising herself. 'I do.'

He smiled then, brilliantly, his eyes a vibrant blue, the strong lines of his face filled with charm. He drew the quilt over her and walked to the door. 'I'll call the doctor.'

'There's no need,' she said. 'Please ... Mr Eliot, please!'

He halted, turning his black head. 'Please ... Mark.'

She swallowed. 'Mark.'

There was a moment while they looked at each other across the room. 'Will you trust me to bandage your ankle, then?'

She nodded.

'I'll get that tea,' he said, going out, and Helen lay back against the pillow, sighing. He was a most disturbing man, and she knew it was madness to allow him to stay here in the house alone with her, but she was tired. Her ankle throbbed with a pain which seemed to have invaded her whole body, weakening her usual strength of will.

With luck, she thought, Paul would be back at any moment. He should have left the factory by now. She bit her lip, hoping he would not fly into a temper when he saw Mark Eliot. He would very likely consider it a strange coincidence that it should be Eliot who found her after her accident.

The door opened and Mark came into the room with a tray. He glanced at her quickly, his eyes so shrewd that she felt he could read her mind, looking away, flushing. He handed her a cup of tea and then began to attend to her swollen ankle. She tried to suppress the wince which his light touch brought and he said curtly, 'Drink your tea,' as though he was aware of her pain and annoyed by it.

Helen drank the tea, eyes lowered, while he bathed and then bandaged her ankle with cool, expert fingers. 'Keep your weight off it for a few days,' he said. 'No bones broken, just some bruising.'

'It feels better already,' she said. 'Thank you for being so kind.'

His hands stroked her exposed calf and she felt a shiver of response run through her, despising herself for it.

'You should go now,' she said huskily, drawing away from him.

He surveyed her with a strangely sardonic face. 'You're scared stiff of me, aren't you, Helen?'

Pride stiffened her body. 'Don't be absurd! It's just that the neighbours will talk.'

'They've been talking ever since that husband of yours arrived here,' he said calmly. 'Is that how it's always been? He's had three jobs in as many years. He had good references, though—that puzzled me. Why, I asked myself, did he move so often? Since he started working for me, the answer's been as plain as the nose on your face.' His words broke off and his blue eyes teasingly inspected her features. 'Except that you happen to have quite a delectable little nose, Helen.'

'Don't,' she muttered, turning her face away.

His hand came out to pull her head around towards him. He leaned over to look into her eyes. 'Helen ...'

The door opened behind them and Mark's hand fell from her. He turned and rose at the same moment while she stared at Paul, eyes enormous in her hot face.

Paul was frozen in the doorway, his eyes narrowed. There was a long silence which seemed endless to her.

Then Mark said lightly, 'I'm afraid your wife has had an accident, Eastwood. She fell in the abbey ruins and almost knocked herself out. She has a sprained ankle. It would be wise for her to stay in bed for a day or two.' He walked to the door, his body held tensely. Paul did not move, watching him. At the last moment, though, he shifted aside and Mark nodded to him. 'Goodnight, Mrs Eastwood,' he said politely to her over his shoulder.

Helen somehow managed to make a conventional reply. 'Goodnight, Mr Eliot, and thank you for your help. You've been very kind.'

'How did you come to meet my wife right out there?' Paul asked as Mark was about to walk from the room.

Mark looked almost bored as he faced him. 'I was riding, as I always do, and I saw the accident happen, so I went over to see who it was—she was wearing an anorak and I thought it was a child for a moment.'

Paul nodded thoughtfully. 'Lucky for Helen you came along, then.'

'I've bandaged her ankle. She should be all right. If there's any bad pain she should see a doctor.' Mark gave him a brief nod. 'Goodnight, Eastwood.'

His footsteps sounded in the silence between the husband and wife. When the front door closed Paul gave her a dark smile. 'What was Eliot up to when I so inconveniently arrived, my darling?'

She had had time to control her face. Calmly, she said, 'He'd just finished bandaging my ankle.'

'I thought I detected an atmosphere,' Paul said probingly, watching her. 'Had he made a pass?'

She met his eyes unflinchingly. 'Don't be stupid!'

His mouth thinned in that cruel smile. 'Yes, it would be stupid of him, but then he wouldn't know what a cold-blooded little wretch you are, Helen.' His eyes suddenly sharpened, anger in them, as he glanced around the room. 'My God, you let him bring you in here ... you bitch!'

She lay very still. 'What?'

His face had a glazed red hardness. 'What do you think he deduced from that bed?' he asked unpleasantly.

She bit her lip, remembering Mark's probing looks as he took in the nature of her room.

'You're usually so keen on keeping up appearances, Helen,' Paul added spitefully. 'What made you so careless?' He watched her with a sharp expression. 'Could it be you wanted Eliot to know you were available?'

Helen clenched her hands into fists, then closed her eyes and let tears force themselves between her lids. 'I was in too much pain to care what he thought,' she flung furiously. Her head ached, her ankle throbbed. Paul's malice and cruelty seemed intolerable to her.

Paul came over to the bed and stood there, watching her. She opened her eyes and found him staring at her loosened hair, the fine silvery fall of it over her slender shoulders.

'Eliot is a womaniser,' he said. 'And you're a beautiful woman, Helen. It wouldn't surprise me if he fancied you. So I hope you didn't encourage him to have hopes.'

'Please, go away, Paul,' she said drearily. 'I'm tired and I'm in no mood to listen to any of your scenes at the moment.'

He knelt on the bed and both hands closed around her throat, startling and alarming her. The bright, pale eyes stared into her own. 'Stay away from Eliot, Helen, or I'll make you sorry.' His fingers tightened like steel claws, hurting, impeding her breathing. She gasped painfully, trying to pull his hands away, and they tightened again.

'Paul,' she muttered, half choking, 'you're hurting me!'

A peculiar brightness had come into the pale eyes. He laughed with an excited undertone. 'Poor Helen, am I?' He was making fun of her, she realised, enjoying the pain he was inflicting on her. One of his hands moved away, stroking down over her body until it closed over her small, high breast. She stared, riveted, into his watchful eyes. His fingers deliberately hurt, biting into the warm soft flesh beneath them.

A moan escaped her. 'Please, Paul, don't!'

'Just remember what I said, then,' he said softly. 'If I can't have you, Eliot can't either.'

She shivered at something in his voice.

'I don't like the idea that Eliot knows you don't sleep with me,' Paul said. He released her and walked to the door. 'We must disabuse him some time,' he said ambiguously as he left.

Helen lay back, shuddering. It was not the first time he had been sadistic. Those moments of deliberately inflicted pain came from time to time. He was like a little boy pulling the wings off flies, pleasure in his face, enjoying the sensation of power over something weaker than himself. Paul was aware of his own weakness, angry about it, resentful of the fact that she recognised his failings. He preferred to see the bright godlike image other women reflected as they looked at him. That was the self he wished to see. Her clarity of vision angered him, and anger made him cruel.

Despite Mark Eliot's advice she got up next day and hobbled around the house. Paul would never get up if someone did not call him. He got far too little sleep to be capable of waking himself. He was sullen again that morning, ignoring her, and she was relieved when he had gone.

Karen left Terry with her that afternoon. It gave Helen enormous pleasure to see the child playing with a pack of cards, building frail houses with it with concentration, muttering as they toppled. She took her into the kitchen and they made fairy cakes together, icing them in different colours. When Karen got back Terry was triumphant, displaying the plate of cakes to her mother. Karen admired them, winking discreetly at Helen, and had to taste one with a cup of tea.

Helen was surprised when Paul came home quite early with a bunch of winter roses for her. He kissed her cheek as he handed them to her. 'Helen darling, forgive me.' His pleading was childishly appealing, the pale eyes wide.

She smiled. 'Thank you, Paul. They're lovely.'

'You sit down while I get some supper for us,' he said. 'You shouldn't be walking on that foot.'

He opened a tin of soup, made scrambled egg to follow it, and they ate together in a relatively friendly atmosphere. They watched TV together for a few hours, then he insisted on carrying her up to bed. He left her there and she undressed and got between the sheets. He suddenly came back with a glass of brandy. 'Now, you must drink it,' he said. 'It's medicinal.'

Protesting, she let him lift it to her lips. The warmth flooded through her and she lay back smiling. Paul bent to kiss her and suddenly she could feel the intention hidden behind his handsome face. Her eyes flew to his face. He gave her a peculiar little smile, his hands on her shoulders.

'Goodnight, Paul.' She tried to control the shiver running over her body.

He did not stop smiling. 'Not tonight, Helen,' he whispered, and the pale eyes had a high glitter of excitement. His mouth came down and forced her lips apart. Helen tried to drag her head back, pushing him away, struggling against the avidly possessive hands.

She had no need to search his eyes for signs of

love. She had known for a long time that Paul did not love her, did not know what love meant. He called it love when he meant a greedy desire to enjoy her body.

'No,' she muttered, sickened.

'You exposed our marriage to Eliot. I can't stand the man. I won't have him knowing that my wife won't share my bed. You should never have brought him in here, let him see you sleep alone.'

'Mark Eliot has nothing to do with this! Our marriage was a desert before we came to Ryethorpe.'

'You made it one!'

'I did? I've been the one who held it together for the last two years, but you've never tried to make a real marriage out of it.'

'I'm trying now,' Paul said with a tart smile.

'You call this an effort to make our marriage work?' Helen looked at him with contempt. 'I'm in pain, I'm tired and I just want to go to sleep, but you want to force yourself on me?'

He drew back, his face glazed, his eyes searching her face while he still held her immobile against her pillows.

'You're my wife. I need you.'

'You need a woman, any woman. You've never needed me, Paul—not me as myself, just my body to relieve a temporary urge, just as you've done with others. That isn't marriage, it's legalised prostitution!'

Paul's face flooded with dark colour. He actually looked shocked, his blue eyes widening and darkening.

'That's a rotten thing to say!'

'It's the truth.'

'No!' He shook her violently and her hair flew across the pillow in a pale, glittering swathe. 'I love you!'

'Did you love me when you slept with my best friend?'

'She was never your friend or she wouldn't have gone after me.'

Helen closed her eyes, shivering. 'Paul, for God's sake! Don't blame her. Are you always the one who's innocent? Grow up—start seeing things as they really are.'

There was a silence. Paul's hands tightened on her, then slowly relaxed and released her. He straightened, staring at her. 'You hate me, don't you?'

She looked at him sadly. 'No, Paul, I don't hate you.'

Their eyes held in a wordless knowledge. Paul's bones tightened beneath the pale skin of his face. 'You're just indifferent,' he translated slowly, seeing the tired greyness of her features.

Helen didn't answer; her face was even whiter than his, her eyes filled with regret. 'I'm tired.'

He pushed a shaking hand through his hair. 'You did love me,' he said almost to himself. 'You could again.'

They had reached the first moment when Helen really felt that Paul might be beginning to take their marriage seriously. Slowly she put a hand on his arm, looking at him hard. 'You know how I feel about divorce. I don't want to leave you, Paul, but it's no good if only one of us tries to make the marriage work. You aren't trying. You never have.'

His eyes moved away, then came back to her face. 'And if I do try? What sort of marriage are you planning, Helen? Is it part of your scheme that I'm to sleep alone for the rest of my life?'

'No,' she said with a reluctance that tasted sour in her mouth. 'But you've made promises before and haven't kept them.'

'So I must wait, must I? Prove I love you?' His voice had a sharp ring, his face was empty.

Silently she shrugged. He knew precisely what she meant. Paul studied her as if she were a strange creature about whom he was curious. After a pause he said: 'While you're working for Eliot I don't want him learning any more about our marriage than he already has, Helen. While he was here I saw the way he looked at you. Stay away from him.'

'I've no intention of getting involved with another man,' she said drily. 'I've had all I can take from you.'

His face empty, he stood up. 'How long am I going to have to wait?'

'Until I'm sure you mean what you say.'

He nodded and walked out. She shivered as she stared at the closed door. She had told the truth when she had said she did not hate him. She was sorry for him. She was saddened by him, but if he had taken her she would have hated it. She found his lovemaking repulsive—it was empty of everything which had any connection with love as Helen recognised it. It was self-willed greed, a physical urge which would have scarred her if she had been forced to submit to the possession of that handsome, selfish and loveless man. She had promised to stay with him, promised to make yet another attempt to help their marriage to survive. If Paul kept his side of the bargain she would keep hers—but she did not know how she was going to bear it.

CHAPTER FIVE

ALTHOUGH she was able to hobble around the house, her ankle was not strong enough for her to begin work as arranged the following Monday, and Paul brought her a message from Mark Eliot insisting that she should not start working for him until she was able to walk normally. It was a fortnight before she took up the job. She arrived to find the office empty. Deirdre, she already knew, had gone; departed for London and a more exciting life, promising to leave Helen a list of instructions. Helen searched for it but found no trace. Deirdre, she assumed, had forgotten.

Standing in the centre of the room, Helen felt nervous apprehension. This was going to make her new job difficult—she had no idea how to run this office apart from the usual little routine of opening mail and answering the telephone.

Mark Eliot strode into the room but halted as he saw her. 'Good morning.' He was in shirt sleeves, a smudge of grease along one cheek, his hair ruffled, and had clearly been working for some time.

'Good morning, Mr Eliot,' Helen said politely. 'I suppose you wouldn't know if Deirdre left any notes for me? I can't find them.'

He laughed curtly. 'You don't surprise me.' The blue eyes stayed level on her face. 'Hang on while I wash, then I'll help you out as far as I can.'

She heard water running in his office. Sitting

down, she waited. He came back, his sleeves rolled back to his elbow, drying his hands and face on a towel. 'One of the machines went haywire.' He tossed the towel through the door with a casual gesture and turned back to her. 'Now,' he said, surveying her. 'I have a pretty clear idea of the routine.'

He had more than that, she realised, listening to him for the next ten minutes. Helen wondered if he knew as much about every other job as he did about this one. She had never worked anywhere before where the boss knew the office routine as well as any secretary. Usually they waved a vague hand and said: 'You'll pick it up.' Mark Eliot not only knew where everything was kept; he could use it. Sitting down at her desk, he typed out a brisk list which she could use as a guide in future and his speed was almost as rapid as her own.

Looking up, he caught her eyes on him and grinned suddenly at her surprise. 'Yes, I can type. I can use any machine I have on the premises.' Spreading his long fingers, he said with dry self-amusement, 'Since I was able to walk I've been fascinated by machines. I love to get my hands on a new one.'

'A useful interest.'

He nodded. 'It comes in handy. I can also mend them if they start having hiccups. Of course I have mechanics and engineers on the staff, but I wouldn't ask them to do a job I can't do myself.'

'They don't mind if you do their jobs?'

He grimaced. 'The unions occasionally get temperamental about it, but I'm careful not to antagonise them too much. I don't have much trouble with them. We treat each other warily.'

Anyone with any sense would treat this man

warily, Helen thought, watching him as he finished
typing the list. He gave off a hum of energy like a
machine, his mind and body tensed and poised for
action, the blue eyes quick and keen, the hard face
betraying determination.

He got up, glancing at his watch. 'Well, I'll leave
you to deal with things as well as you can. I shan't
expect miracles at this stage. If you need any further
help, shout. I've got some phone calls to make.'

He gave her a brief smile. It was polite rather
than friendly. Helen watched him close his door.
She felt relief. She had been afraid she would not
be able to keep distance between them, but it ap-
peared that Mark Eliot intended to do that of his
own accord.

There was a world of difference between the
charming, slightly impudent man she had met on
her first day here and the man who had just gone
through that door.

Now that she worked for him she came, it seemed,
into a new category. She need not have been
alarmed.

As the day wore on she grew more and more at
ease, feeling, in fact, slightly foolish when she remembered her uneasiness before she arrived. Mark
established a working relationship calmly, coolly,
without haste or undue emphasis, and she found it
easy to slide into the same manner.

Office routine differs little from place to place.
The same tasks need to be done, the same neces-
sities dictate a pattern. Helen found she was soon
adjusting to her new role. Gradually as the afternoon turned towards an autumnal sunset she found
herself enjoying the work. Helen liked doing things

well. Even in housework she needed to feel she was capable, abreast of the job.

Glancing at the clock, she began to tidy her desk. Mark came out and stood watching her covering her typewriter. 'Well done,' he said quietly. 'You picked it up with remarkable speed.'

'It wasn't difficult.'

He smiled. 'Deirdre wouldn't have agreed with you.'

Helen swept a glance over her clear desk. 'She found Ryethorpe too quiet for her, I gathered.'

'Yes, the big city lured. I hope she finds what she's looking for.' He sounded cynical, dry.

'I expect she will.' Helen was half thinking of something else, her mind on what she would meet when she got home. Paul was going to be extra difficult tonight; she had seen it in his eye this morning. He was annoyed because she was starting work for Mark Eliot. She had half feared that he would come into the office during the day, but he hadn't put in an appearance.

'You think we all do?' Mark sounded wry.

She glanced at him, baffled. 'Do what?'

'Find what we're looking for.' He gave her a long stare, his eyes sharp.

Helen flushed at something in his eyes, his tone. 'I suppose that depends on what we're looking for.'

He pushed his hands into his pockets, standing there poised and casual, a very tall lean man with a hard-bitten face. 'What are you looking for?'

'My coat, at the moment,' she said lightly, glancing across the office at it. 'Time I went.'

He neither pressed the matter nor commented, but watched her as she got ready to go. 'Goodnight,' she said, and he answered in a tone as calm as her own.

Paul arrived an hour after her and as soon as she heard the bang of the door she knew what sort of mood he would be in as he walked into the kitchen. His eyes leapt at her across the room, searching her face as though he would find evidence of her feelings in it. Helen carefully kept it blank.

'Enjoyed your day?' he asked with a sneer.

'It was difficult at first, but I coped.' She continued to get the evening meal ready, aware of him watching her all the time.

'I hope you kept Eliot in his place.' That came out with a hiss and she shot him a quick look.

'I didn't need to—he's my boss and he made it plain.'

Paul's face worked harshly. 'I hope you're telling the truth. If I find out you're lying ...'

'How much longer are we going to keep this up?' She turned on him, her face flushing. 'If you want me to chuck the job in, say so. If you don't, shut up!'

She saw the surprise in his face. 'Don't talk to me like that!'

'I just want some peace,' Helen said sharply. 'Make up your mind, Paul. You can't have your cake and eat it. If you want to make trouble about the job I'll give in my resignation tomorrow.'

He drew in his lower lip, sulkily staring at her. Paul liked having a stick to beat her with and he did not want to give it up. At last he shrugged. 'O.K., forget it. You haven't got enough blood in your veins to start anything with Eliot, anyway.'

They ate their meal in an almost unbroken silence. Paul got up afterwards and hovered, looking restless. 'Shall we watch television?' Helen suggested. 'There's a good play on tonight.'

'I promised to see a customer,' said Paul, not quite meeting her eyes. 'I won't be long.'

When he had gone she felt a deep relief. They had nothing, she thought. Not a thing. They might as well be total strangers. Alone, they never spoke. Paul knew as much of what went on inside her head as he would do of someone he saw in a bus, and she knew too much of what went on inside his head. He was a shallow Narcissus; vain, childish, needing constant distraction. He had the attention span of a child, always growing bored, always restless, needing the constant reflection of himself in new eyes in order to find even himself real. The open vanity of children could be touching, lovable. In a grown man it was saddening.

That first day established the pattern of all the others. Each morning Helen drove with Paul to the factory, opened up the office, worked with Mark Eliot on the same calm, friendly level and went back home in the evenings to do a little housework and cook an evening meal. Sometimes Paul came home; more often he didn't. Helen never asked where he was or showed any interest. Slowly she realised that Paul was involved with someone else. It didn't hurt this time; it was merely a relief. His interest in her lapsed into a vague hostility tempered with faint uneasiness. He avoided her eyes when they were alone. He had always done so when he was seeing someone else. In the past it had hurt; now Helen couldn't care less.

She had known it would happen. If she had given in to his temporary desire for her, sooner or later he would have strayed again. Paul could not maintain a relationship for long. He grew too bored. The daily routine of work irked him; he needed the constant excitement of new faces, new pursuits. Had he had any real feelings for her he would have stayed faithful. He hadn't even been able to pretend for a matter of days.

It gave her no particular satisfaction to know she had been right. She merely noted the fact wryly, grateful for the relaxation of tension which his distraction gave her. Paul was easier to live with when he was elsewhere absorbed. He would only become spiteful, difficult, sullen when his new affair palled and he began to look around for newer interests and to feel both guilty and irritated with her.

Three weeks after she had begun to work for Mark Eliot she found Paul busy packing a case one morning. Helen stared at him and he gave her a brusque look. 'I'm going to Tokyo,' he said. 'My flight is at eleven. Can you give me a hand?'

'When was this decided? You didn't mention it before.' She went over and glanced into his case with lifted brows. Lifting all the things out, she said drily, 'I'll do it. Just get what you need and lay it on the bed. If you pack the clothes like that they'll be creased by the time you unpack them.'

Paul moved around the room, fetching clothes. 'I'll be gone for around a week.'

'Was it a sudden decision?'

'No. I just forgot.'

He had forgotten to mention it because they never talked, they never said anything to each other but the brief remarks of strangers living in one house. Helen deftly, quickly packed his things. He watched her, now and then looking at his watch, his movements restless. When she had finished he came and locked the case, lifted it.

'I'll send you a postcard,' he said. After a little pause he added with a touch of spite, 'You won't miss me.'

She didn't answer that. What could she say? How could you miss someone who was never there anyway and even if he was never said anything?

When he had gone she went into his room to tidy the wreckage he had left behind. A trail of confusion lay across the room. Helen hurriedly picked things up, folded them, put them back into drawers and cupboards. She hated untidiness. She had an orderly mind. It annoyed Paul who didn't care if he lived in a whirlwind of disorder. Helen's instincts were always to organise, to bring order out of chaos. She could not sit down in an untidy room. It nagged away at her all the time until she had to get up and make it tidy. The beauty of order seemed to her important. Machines ought to work. Rooms ought to look elegant and comfortable. Helen liked things in a proper place, a place designed for them.

When she was at work later the thought was still in her head. Mark came into the room to give her a memo to type and watched her delicately cleaning her typewriter keys. 'Having trouble?'

'No, just making sure the type cuts cleanly.'

'I'd noticed how much better the letters look these days,' he said with a smile.

'Thank you,' she said, smiling back. 'I like things to work as they should.'

'Machines repay attention,' Mark said drily. 'People aren't so easy, are they?'

'People aren't predictable. Machines are.'

'But much as I like them, machines aren't as rewarding as people,' he said quietly. 'Don't get sidetracked, Helen.'

She looked at him in bewilderment. 'Sidetracked?'

'Into imagining that you can exist without people. You can't—none of us can.'

Her colour rose suddenly. 'I didn't suggest we could.'

'You didn't have to. It's implicit in your whole attitude.'

Helen looked away from him. They were treading on thin ice. He saw too clearly. He saw too much. It was not the first time she had realised it, but the calm working relationship they had achieved had blocked it from her mind. Now her awareness of him came back and with it her feeling of alarm. Mark Eliot was dangerous to her.

Softly, behind her, he said: 'You're a very orderly creature, Helen. You like rules and you keep them religiously, don't you? You wouldn't still be married to Eastwood if you didn't.'

'But I am still married to him,' she broke in huskily.

'Is it a form of masochism?' His voice was dry. 'Does it give you a perverted pleasure to take what he dishes out?'

'My marriage isn't a subject I want to discuss.' Helen closed the typewriter and stood up, coming too close to him in the movement, her eyes meeting his in a straight and level stare.

'You're building on sand, Helen. The house will crumble.'

'That's my affair.' She kept her eyes expressionless. 'Please, don't talk about it. We agreed that it had nothing to do with you.'

'I didn't agree to anything of the kind. No man is an island.' He smiled abruptly, the blue eyes dancing in that wicked, amused smile he so rarely gave her these days. 'No woman, either. We're all involved with each other. Indifference is a form of blasphemy, to my mind. We have no right to see others suffer and not care.'

'I'm not suffering!'

'Don't prickle,' he said gently. 'It's no sin to have feelings, to be human. We all breathe the same air, Helen.'

She looked away. 'I must wash my hands. They're filthy.'

He smiled with dry appreciation of the change of subject and moved back to let her pass.

When she came back and typed his memo she took it in to him and Mark's manner had returned to the usual formal courtesy which made life easier for her. She was grateful, realising how careful he was being to keep that distance between them. Their brief exchange earlier had shown her only too clearly that if either of them moved an inch closer there could be a real problem. The sexual attraction which she had been aware of from the start was only the tip of the iceberg. Beneath the calm waters of their daily relationship moved something far more dangerous, far more destructive in potential.

It was comparatively easy to douse down the sexual smouldering which she knew Mark had aroused in her, but she would not find it easy to fight that other, more powerful knowledge. The chill emptiness of her marriage had as its cause the total lack of understanding, mental contact, between herself and Paul. All that was missing between her and Paul was present between herself and Mark. Without speaking they could communicate. A look, a word and their minds lay open to each other.

That was where the danger lay. One could ignore the drag of the senses, but one could not shut off that other magnetism. It went on all the time beneath their quiet faces, their restrained manners. Daily they grew to know each other better. The more she knew of him the more she liked him, respected him, admired him.

It was something she had not bargained for when she started work. She had hoped to resist the physical temptation. She had not even suspected the permanent draining temptation which real mental accord could offer.

Loneliness was sapping. Helen lived and breathed in a hollow world where she was neither free nor bound by any real ties. Her marriage to Paul chained her, yet left her alone.

Seeing Mark every day, talking to him, knowing that she got back from him the mental spark which had never flowed between herself and Paul, she came to recognise with an even greater despair her own loneliness.

People need people—it was a trite little phrase,

but it summed it up. She was so tired of existing on an emotional desert island, fruitlessly sending out messages which never drew a reply.

Paul's absence in Tokyo meant nothing to her. She barely noticed he had gone. The only difference was that his room stayed tidy, his possessions were no longer scattered idly around the house, she was not woken at some unearthly hour of the night by hearing him stumbling around swearing.

While he was away she took the opportunity of doing some decorating in his room. It occupied the evenings, and Paul would not be there to complain that he couldn't stand the smell of fresh paint or that she had interfered with one of his possessions.

It took her three nights, but when it was done she was pleased with the way it looked. She had carefully chosen wallpaper she thought Paul would like and she had bought new lampshades and curtains for the room.

It would be a surprise for him when he got back, she thought, looking around the room with a smile.

One of the things Helen felt the lack of most of all was of that giving which comes with a loving relationship. Her parents had loved birthdays, getting ready for them for weeks beforehand, smuggling parcels into the house, going around with secret smiles. Helen had been taught to get happiness in giving as well as receiving and had found it the deepest pleasure to give. She remembered so many times when her father had crept up behind her mother, winking at Helen over her unsuspecting head, with a prettily wrapped parcel in his hands. The joy, the laughter, the shared delight, had given a golden light to all their lives. Paul had never known how to give or even to receive. He took as if by right and seemed to imagine that that was all he had to do.

The morning after she finished her decorating she was typing when a young girl bounded into the room following an enormous shaggy grey and white dog of some indeterminate ancestry.

Helen looked up, surprised.

'Hi,' the girl said. 'Uncle Mark in? You must be Helen. We've all heard how efficient you are. Uncle Mark is much happier since Deirdre went. She was a terrible drag, wasn't she? Buster, sit! Sit, Buster!' Buster lolled a vast pink tongue and tried to climb up Helen's desk. The girl gave her a deprecating little grin. 'Well, sometimes he sits. I'm training him.'

'He can do with it.' Mark's voice was light and amused. 'What are you doing here, brat?'

Girl and dog went across the room in a great tidal rush and both ended up attached with loving enthusiasm to him. Over their heads he grinned at Helen.

'Down, both of you,' he said in mock wrath. 'Helen, this is my niece Patsy. Patsy, this is Helen Eastwood, my secretary.'

Patsy disentangled herself from the lead on which her dog was dragging as he tried to cover Mark's averted face with passionate kisses.

'Sit, Buster!' she said desperately.

'*Sit!*' Mark's roar surprised the dog into obedience. He lowered his rump to the ground and panted cheerfully as he gazed at Mark with open admiration.

Patsy smiled at Helen. 'Hello again.'

'Hello.' Helen remembered Mark saying that his niece loved treacle pudding. The girl was still faintly plump, her dark hair flowing loose from a small, sallow-skinned little face which had a certain charm. Her eyes were as blue as her uncle's and held laughter as she looked at Helen.

'Buster has a mind of his own.'

'She can see that,' Mark commented drily. 'And I'm still waiting to hear what you two are doing in my office when I'm busy.'

'I'm taking him for a walk and we were passing,' she said with a hopeful little smile at him.

'You're taking *him* for a walk?' The dark brows lifted ironically. 'That's a fable, Patsy. That monstrous animal is taking you. Why don't you put a saddle on him and ride him? He's as big as a donkey.'

Patsy laughed. 'You're cruel. Isn't he cruel, Helen? Poor old Buster! Look at him gazing at you with loving eyes.' She rumpled the rough thick coat and the dog turned to gaze at her instead. Patsy dropped a kiss on his enormous head.

'Shall I get some coffee, Mr Eliot?' Helen suggested.

Mark smiled at her. 'I suppose we must entertain our guests. Thank you, Helen.'

Patsy greeted the coffee with enthusiasm when Helen handed her the cup. She was sitting in Mark's office with Buster lying across her feet. Helen produced a plastic bowl of water and the dog eagerly drank some.

'Now how did you manage that?' asked Mark, grinning.

'It's the base of a flower pot,' Helen explained.

'Very clever,' he admired, and she laughed as she went out.

As Patsy departed a quarter of an hour later she paused to thank Helen for the coffee and Buster's bowl of water. 'See you,' she said as she vanished in the dog's plunging wake, and Helen smiled after her as the door slammed.

'What do you think of her?' Mark asked from the door.

'She's very sweet.' Helen turned her head and their eyes met. Mark smiled at her again, slowly, and her heart missed a beat. He went back into his office and she stared at the door, her eyes haunted.

Later that afternoon while he was dictating to her he paused between letters to say: 'My mother would like to meet you. Will you come to dinner, Helen?'

He had phrased it in a way which made it hard to refuse without discourtesy. Slowly she said, 'Thank you, I'd like to.'

Mark's blue eyes were keen. 'Don't sound so worried. The whole family will be there. You won't be exposed to any danger.'

She flushed. 'I didn't . . .'

'Oh, yes, you did,' he said in that dry voice. 'Let's be honest, Helen. We both know why you hesitated before you accepted. I'm telling you the truth —my mother did ask me to invite you. When you meet her you'll know why.' He grinned abruptly with the amusement which altered his whole face. 'My mother likes to keep her finger on the pulse of the firm. She's a matriarch and proud of it.'

'You aren't the eldest?' Helen thought of Patsy. 'Your niece doesn't live with you?'

'Patsy's mother is three years older than me. Anne was a twin—her twin died at birth. I've often wondered if that affected her.'

Helen looked puzzled. 'In what way?'

'Anne has never seemed complete.' He had a serious expression. 'She has a sort of vagueness as if she wasn't sure she was real.'

'I know the feeling.' As soon as she had said it Helen flushed, wishing she hadn't. Mark looked down at her, eyes narrowing.

'I thought you might,' he said calmly.

Hurriedly she asked: 'Where does your sister live?'

'In the town, about half a mile from here. Anne's husband Frank is a solicitor. They won't be at the dinner because they're in London. Patsy is staying with us while they're away.'

'Hence her visit?'

He smiled. 'Hence her visit.' He paused. 'To-night would suit us if it will suit you.'

Helen felt an instant rush of alarm and struggled with it. She did not want to get any more involved with him than she already was, but she could hardly say so.

'Or are you fully booked up for the near future?' he asked in a sardonic tone which made it clear he knew very well she wasn't and could read her mind as clearly as if her head were made of crystal.

'I'd love to come,' she made herself say as coolly as he was speaking.

'Right,' he said without emphasis, and at once continued with his dictation. When he had finished he told her he would drive her to his home when they had stopped work. Helen looked doubtfully at her simple grey dress and he said lightly, 'You look fine.' A pause and he added as calmly, 'You always do. I never tire of looking at you.'

Helen could find nothing to say in reply to that. Her heart missed another beat and did not slow down for a long time afterwards. She wished Mark had not said it, and yet she was stupidly happy because he had. It was a feeling she had had for a long time. She was never tired of looking at him, either. Whenever she thought he would not realise it she looked at him with pleasure and sadness. Her eyes constantly traced the strong, hard bones beneath his weatherbeaten brown skin, the faint arrogance of his nose, the humour his mouth could reveal, the determined thrust of his jawline. It all added up to a portrait of a man complete in himself; a man of enormous willpower and certainty, whose charm was never synthetic or conscious, whose kindness was unforced and genuine, whose strength came from an inner source unpoisoned by self.

Before joining him to drive home that evening she spent some time giving her reflection in the cloakroom a coolly immaculate discretion which she hoped would get her through the evening.

Mark surveyed her when she returned for a long moment, a faint dry smile on his lips. 'Charming,' he said on a note of mockery.

She could not hope to hide from him what had been in her mind as she brushed back her hair into a taut chignon. Her quiet calmness held no secrets for him.

Don't come so close, she thought, looking away from him. He had not moved and yet she felt an intangible connection between them, as though his hands had touched her cheek or brushed her hair.

They drove through a grey evening, mist blowing wetly in gusts across the car windscreen. 'Does it ever stop raining?' she asked.

'It has been a wet autumn,' he agreed.

'And looks like being a wetter winter.'

He smiled at her sideways. 'Wait and see. I never care to prophesy the weather here.'

His home lay just outside the town on a long scar of moorland which should have dwarfed and silenced it and yet which merely gave the strong stone outline a defiant look, as though it faced the elements and challenged them boldly. Weathered to a mellow cream, the walls had once been painted white. They were deep and thick, Helen was to discover later, built to withstand anything the wind and rain could throw at them.

The dripping trees bent over the car as they sped up the drive, brushing long wet fingers against the top of it with a melancholy delicacy. Mark drew up outside the house and looked at her. 'Welcome to my home.' The words were coolly uttered but deliberate. The blue eyes emphasised them.

'Is it old?' she asked, turning away from what she read in his gaze.

'Old enough. This particular version was built in 1854, but there was a house here before that—it burnt down, I'm told. There were thatched stables at the rear and a groom set them alight one night— a candle blowing over, probably. The fire spread from them to the house.'

'Did the horses escape?' Helen asked, and Mark gave her an amused smile.

'I've no idea. I never thought to ask.'

'I remember when I read *Black Beauty* that I had nightmares for ages afterwards because of the fire in the stables. There's something so terrifying about fire.'

'Yes,' he agreed. 'All uncontrolled forces terrify.'

Helen felt a shiver run down her spine. Mark's head turned and they looked at each other in a silence which was like a vacuum around them, enclosing them alone for that moment.

'Shall we go in?' His voice broke the silence and the mood. They got out of the car and ran through the damp mist to the house. The moment the door opened to admit them Helen felt the warmth, the atmosphere of a family home. It had an elegance which was unstrained, faded brocades in delicate colours, deep cushioned chairs and couches, dogs underfoot, fires leaping in grates, people talking all at once so that Helen could only stand and stare and try to sort them all out.

She had met Robby Eliot several times since the night they were introduced at the country club. He grinned at her admiringly, a hand holding Buster back as he surged eagerly to get at Mark. Joanne, too, was immediately recognisable, her pale beautiful little face wistful between those strands of straight dark hair. Patsy she found smiling at her with the warmth she had been shown earlier that day. From her Helen's eyes moved to the thin white-haired woman in a blue dress who was pronouncing vehemently, 'Mark, the chimneys need sweeping. We've had a torrent of soot in the drawing-room and it's taken an hour to clear it up.'

Patsy chimed in, 'The dogs went crazy. Buster looked like a sweep's brush. He dashed about barking like mad.'

'I'll get the sweep on to it tomorrow,' Mark promised, taking Helen's elbow. 'Quiet, all of you! Mother, this is Helen. Helen, my mother.'

Everyone was quiet as Helen and Mrs Eliot shook hands, but Helen felt it was the lull before the storm broke out again. The family had an aggregate strength which was far more than their individual parts. She sensed that they were a unit, facing the world together, surer of their roles in life because of that very unity. That they all regarded Mark as the head of that one body was obvious in the way they all moved to meet him when he came home, the way in which he was given the responsibility for the arrival of the sweep.

Mrs Eliot's eyes were piercing Helen's face as she murmured a polite welcome. Helen could see now where all the blue eyes in the family had come from —they dominated and gave an unaltered beauty to Mrs Eliot's thin face. She had a strong resemblance to her elder son, her jaw and nose as powerful, even more striking in her thin female face. Helen felt her personality like a blow. Mrs Eliot was not a woman one would forget when one had once met her.

'I gather you're a newcomer to the north, Mrs Eastwood,' the clear cool voice murmured.

Helen smiled. 'Yes. My first visit.'

'You've picked a bad winter. We don't always get weather like this—although you may not believe that now.'

'She wondered if it ever stopped raining here,' Mark said with quiet enjoyment.

'It does,' Mrs Eliot nodded. 'And when it does this is a very beautiful place.'

'So there,' Mark drawled, grinning. 'You've been told, Helen. Make even a passing and gentle criticism of Yorkshire and you get your knuckles rapped.'

His mother turned her blue eyes on him with regal displeasure. 'Take her coat, Mark. She's wet.' She touched Helen's arm. 'Come to the fire, my dear. You look chilled.'

'She is,' said Mark with a faint dry emphasis which made both his mother and Helen look at him. His mother frowned. Helen looked hurriedly away.

Robby Eliot followed them, but Joanne and Patsy trailed after Mark as he took Helen's coat away, their voices oddly similar as they talked to him, the dogs at their heels. Buster glanced round at the orange flames of the fire, looked back at Mark's departing figure and then with a gusty sigh followed him too.

'Can I get you a drink, Helen?' Robby asked, smiling at her as she took a seat by the fire.

'Thank you,' she smiled back at him.

'Sherry? Sweet or dry?'

'Sweet,' she said without enthusiasm.

He went off and his mother asked Helen: 'If you would prefer something else, we have quite a wide selection. Mark drinks whisky.'

'I really don't drink at all,' Helen admitted, her eyes on Mrs Eliot's commanding face. Once, she thought, this must have been an exceptionally beautiful woman. The remnants of that beauty lay in her face now, was suggested by her facial structure, the bones and fine proportions of eyes, nose, mouth.

The beauty had not so much gone as suffered a sea change—having been transmuted into an age-less appeal which would only deepen with time. This is how Mark will look as he grows old, Helen thought, and was so deeply struck by the realisation that she stared in startled surprise. Paul, when he aged, would lose the golden mask he showed the world. Mark's beauty came from within and would increase. She wondered what on earth Paul would be like when he lost his male beauty. The selfish shallow nature would show then, rising like a dis-turbing scum to the surface of his features.

Mrs Eliot returned Helen's gaze calmly. 'Mark sings your praises very highly, Mrs Eastwood. Your husband works for us too, I believe.'

Helen felt herself flushing. 'Yes.' She knew that Mrs Eliot must be very well aware of that. The question had had other purposes than to elicit such a fact.

'You have no children?'

'No,' Helen said quietly, trying to hide the pain that question gave her, her eyes level.

'Would you like some?'

For a moment Helen almost spoke sharply, an-gered by the question. She drew a shaky breath. 'Yes,' she said flatly, deciding to tell the truth. 'But it would not be possible.'

Mrs Eliot frowned. 'What a pity! Have you taken advice on that?'

Helen saw then what she imagined had been meant and almost smiled in rage and grief. Instead she said quietly, 'In a sense, yes.'

The advice she had taken had been her own—
the realisation that it would be criminal to bring
children into such a troubled situation.

'What do you mean, in a sense?' Mrs Eliot held
her eyes, her brows knitted. Helen could see that no
question of privacy ever entered the other woman's
head. Mrs Eliot was interested in the subject, so
she demanded to know the answers to her questions
and never considered if she had a right to ask them.

A movement behind them made them both turn.
Mark stood there, his face stern. He looked at
Helen briefly and then at his mother. 'If the Spanish
Inquisition is over I'll take Helen to see the house.'

His mother flushed slightly. Helen was touched
to see that proud and confident though Mrs Eliot
might be, she was yet capable of accepting criticism,
however gently given, from her son.

'I'm sorry, Mrs Eastwood,' she said now, her chin
lifted in self-irritation. 'I had no right to ask you.'

'Please, forget it,' Helen said, embarrassed and
confused. She smiled. 'It was a natural question.'

Mark guided her away, his hand almost under
her elbow yet not touching her. They did not go
alone. The dogs and Patsy came with them. Patsy
kept up a permanent chorus of remarks as Mark
showed Helen each room. Helen was grateful for
Patsy's presence. It made it easier for her. She felt
able to exclaim with real pleasure as she looked at
pictures, books, smoothly polished old furniture.
The house had a personality which the family had
somehow intensified by their choice of possessions.
Nothing was glaringly new or extravagantly valu-
able. Slightly shabby, well kept and comfortable,
the house wore a welcoming atmosphere lightly. It

was a home and meant as such, a place where dogs and children were not out of place, where people lived happily.

They ended up in Mark's study, a large book-lined room dominated by an old desk covered with papers. He lit a lamp and the room took on a warm cosiness which emphasised the dark night pressing at the windows, the sound of the wind crying on the moors. The telephone suddenly burst into clamour and Patsy turned and fled, shrieking, 'It's for me, it's for me!' The dogs went with her, barking every step of the way. A sudden pandemonium broke loose and Helen started to laugh.

Mark grinned at her. 'Yes, it's a madhouse.'

'I envy you.' The words escaped before she knew what she was going to say.

His face quietened. They stared at each other. The wind blew rain along the windows and a branch scraped along the wall outside. Helen's heart beat harshly against her breastbone as she looked into his eyes. Mark's hand moved up and his fingers trailed lightly along her cheek. It was a gentle caress, tentative and yet deliberate, intended to comfort. It affected her so deeply that her heart seemed to stop and then begin to beat fiercely, demandingly. I love you, she thought, and almost said it, the words burning to escape, and then a tremor of shock ran through her as she realised what she was thinking, feeling. She had fought it so long that she felt tired and almost desperate to concede defeat. Instead, drawing up the last of her energy, she turned away, and Mark's hand fell to his side.

CHAPTER SIX

THAT realisation dogged her mental footsteps all evening, making the rest of what happened seem distant and remote, so that she listened to the family talk over the dinner table with a face so expressionless and shuttered that even Robby gave up trying to arouse her interest. Helen was almost unaware of what was going on around her. She ate, drank, smiled briefly and was in all other senses absent.

'Buster's claws need clipping,' Patsy told Mark.

'Take him to the vet tomorrow.' Mark poured Helen some more wine, his glance barely touching her face. 'Did you get that little problem sorted out, Rob?'

'With a bit of a struggle,' Robby told him. He turned to his mother and began to tell her about some union argument they had had that morning. Mrs Eliot listened intently, commented, showed a shrewd grasp of the situation.

The ceaseless wind blew and rattled the windows. The dogs lay in supine heaps around the fire. Joanne caught Helen's eye and Helen saw the nervous way she hurriedly looked aside. In a flash of intuition she recognised the look in Joanne's eyes as guilt. Was the girl still brooding over whatever had happened between her and Paul? The vulnerable lines of her young face made Helen's heart ache. How had Paul been cruel enough to cause such a young girl any pain?

Looking down at her food, she suddenly wondered if the guilt were all because of a past, brief romance. Surely Paul wasn't still seeing Joanne? Helen had somehow imagined that that had all ended long ago. Or had it? Was Joanne the unknown who was keeping him so busy lately? She looked up and again found Joanne looking at her, again the girl looked hastily away. Oh, no, Helen thought. Surely she can't be so blind, so stupid, as to go on seeing him?

Joanne was so young. The young are blind, their eyes sealed by the generosity of their spirit, the optimism which has not yet been shattered by experience. It was sickening that only someone so young and vulnerable could be open to the sort of pain Paul could inflict. Tougher, more knowledgeable women could get amusement and temporary pleasure from him without getting hurt. Paul flirted without discretion or selection. Helen did not care if he was having an affair with a woman as shallow and heartless as himself—but if he had embroiled a child like Joanne it would be shameful.

Considering her wine glass as though fascinated by it, she wondered how she was to find out. She could hardly ask Joanne, and if she asked Paul he would lie and smile, imagining jealousy.

She could drop a hint to Mark, but if her suspicions were all unfounded she might cause Joanne further unhappiness, and she did not want to do that. Frowning, she fingered the stem of her glass and only just managed to realise that Mrs Eliot was speaking to her.

'Do you miss London, Mrs Eastwood?'

Helen looked up, startled. 'Not really,' she answered hurriedly. 'London has its own attractions, but I like it here.'

Mark laughed softly. 'Clever Helen! You gave the right answer. Any other and you would have had to do the washing up.'

'You don't miss the theatres, the shops?' Mrs Eliot pursued, ignoring his teasing.

'Helen is more interested in a quiet life,' Mark said with a sardonic inflection.

'Are you, Mrs Eastwood?' His mother gave him a firm look. 'She can answer for herself.'

'Speak up, Helen,' Robby grinned. 'You're under cross-examination, remember.'

'Anything you say will be taken down and used against you,' Joanne said suddenly, a faint bitterness in her voice.

'Buster wants my chicken bone,' Patsy said hurriedly, with a tact which Helen admired. 'Can he have it, Mark?'

'No, he cannot, and well you know it. Chicken bones can choke him. Buster, go back to the fire and leave Patsy's plate alone.'

Buster departed with melancholy dignity, wagging his tail to show no hard feelings.

'He understands every word you say, Mark,' Patsy congratulated Mark. 'That shows how smart he is.'

'He doesn't need to understand what I say,' Mark came back. 'He knows what I mean.'

'One look,' Patsy said in a deep, deep voice, 'and he hears the master's voice and obeys.'

'I wish you did,' said Mark with amused reproof.

'Didn't your mother ever teach you that children should be seen and not heard?'

'What children?' Patsy looked around her with exaggerated amazement. 'Where?'

'Funny girl,' grinned Mark, pinching her ear. 'Now you can do the washing-up.'

'Load the machine, Patsy,' Mrs Eliot agreed. 'And clear the table.'

The woman in a neat brown dress who had served the meal came in to help Patsy while the rest of the family withdrew. Helen sat with Mrs Eliot by the fire in the drawing-room which still had a very faint smell of soot lingering in the rain-freshened air. The windows had been left open to clear it, but now that they were shut again the air was filled with the twin scents of soot and rain. Mrs Eliot talked to her calmly about the firm, the town, the surrounding countryside.

Helen was relieved when she felt she could look at the clock and say in pretended surprise, 'Goodness, it's getting late!'

'Goodness, it is,' Mark said derisively, rising. 'I'll take you home.'

Helen made polite farewells, thanked Mrs Eliot with real pleasure for the meal and was glad to get away from the house which she felt so deeply and which made her all the more bitterly aware of the emptiness of her own life.

Mark drove silently through the dark, rainy night with his headlights streaming over the wet roads ahead of them. He dipped them whenever he saw another vehicle coming so as not to blind them. On either side of the road the grey walls meandered with unseen fields pressing behind them.

Coming round a corner they almost ran into a strange white object which turned out to be a sheep which had strayed into the road. Mark pulled up abruptly with a jerk and a muttered swear-word. He banged his hand down on the horn and the night was split with raucous sound, but the animal merely leapt up into the air and then turned, obstinately four-square, facing them, a pair of horns visible now in the light of the car. Mark muttered, 'Stupid beast,' and wound down his window. He flapped a hand out of it and shouted, but the long, stupid face merely glared, strange eyes illumined by the headlights. Helen began to laugh. For a moment the laughter was real and a strange release from the tension which had held her all evening, but then it changed appallingly, grew higher, tears springing from her eyes.

'Helen, for God's sake!' Mark swung to her, looking half angry, half distressed.

'I ... I'm sorry. It looked so f—f—funny ...' She tried to halt the shaking laughter, the flow of tears, and her body trembled violently.

Mark moved, catching her shoulders, shaking her. 'Stop it, Helen!' Her fair hair flew back as he shook her and the wet eyes looked at him desperately.

'Oh, God,' Mark said suddenly, hoarsely.

'No!' Helen moaned as he moved again.

The hands holding her shoulders tightened. His dark head came down and their mouths met in an involuntary movement made by them both at the same moment.

The agonising sweetness which flooded into her temporarily deprived her of the ability to think.

His mouth offered so much she had never believed she would ever have—a tenderness which was gentle and caring, a passion which was demanding without selfishness, a love which was deep and strangely kind. Mark's hands slid down her arms and moved round her back, pulling her closer. The warm strong mouth gave and took. Helen held his face between her hands, feeling the strength of his bone structure under her fingers, groaning as his kiss deepened even further. The rain and wind blew outside the car. The silence and darkness increased their isolation, their shared passion. It did not seem to matter any more that this should not be happening. All she knew was that the more and more heated movements of his lips were sending her slightly crazy.

Mark's hands gently pushed under her coat. She felt them moving on her, felt him find her breasts and curve his hands over them in a warm gesture without greed. The fire he had lit inside her was raging now. She whimpered, pressing closer, giving her body to his hands, sighing, urgently returnng the passion he was revealing.

Mark abruptly pulled back, his body shaking, his breathing harsh. 'If we don't stop now we won't stop,' he said thickly, staring at her. 'Sure that's what you want?'

Helen was so feverish she didn't understand him for a moment, staring at him with wide drowsy leaping eyes, her body trembling violently.

Then it hit her and she gave a choked cry and covered her hot face with shaking hands. 'No, no,' she whispered. Sickness grew inside her. He was right—in one more moment they would have been past the point of no return. She thought she had been—if Mark hadn't stopped then she would have given herself to him without a thought. She could still feel the heat coiled inside her body, the burning desire for him which had raged like a forest fire in those moments.

'I thought not.' He sounded terse, harsh.

She didn't move, sitting there with hidden face, trying to stop shaking, feeling both chilled and feverish. As the aching desire faded a numb coldness took its place. The aftermath of such tumultuous passion, she discovered, was a dull ache in the centre of her body which slowly spread to take over her whole nervous system.

The rainy night seemed to invade her head. She heard Mark sigh, heard him light a cigar, the smoke drifting over her head and filling the car with a faintly smoky fragrance.

'Leave him, Helen,' he said quietly. 'Divorce him.'

She shook her head behind her hands.

'It isn't a marriage,' Mark said flintily. 'It's a mockery of the name. You've tried. Where's the shame in failing?'

Her voice was muffled by her cloaking hands. 'I don't know. You're right, of course, but some things aren't easy to rationalise. All my instincts are to try to fight for it—I married him. I feel it has to be partly my fault it's gone wrong. There ought to be something I can do to put it right.'

'I realise I'm only seeing it from the outside, but I'd say you've done everything you can—Eastwood isn't worth the trouble.'

'I married him,' Helen said desperately. 'I can't

explain, Mark. I don't know what stops me. Every time I think of leaving him a mental barrier comes up. Maybe my parents did too good a job on me. I grew up thinking of marriage as a sort of final decision. I can't do it, Mark. I've tried, but each time I've found myself going back to him. I'm responsible for him, I think, as if he were my child rather than my husband. There are still strings between us—I can't cut them.'

In the silence that followed she heard the wind bluster past and rain sweeping along the road.

'You still love him,' Mark said harshly. 'Is that what you're trying to say?' He didn't wait for her to answer but went on, his voice deep and burningly angry. 'My God, women astonish me! How can they be so blind and stupid? The man's a first-class swine, yet you take his lies, his adulteries, his cruelty, and go back for more. Are you trying for a martyr's crown, Helen?'

She rubbed her shaking hands over her wet face. She hated Mark's anger, his contempt, but she knew it was safer to let him believe that she still cared for Paul than to have him know that tonight she had had to face the fact that she was desperately in love with himself.

Huskily she said: 'We'd better go.'

'Yes.' Mark said that with grinding rage. He flung his cigar out of the window and she heard the hiss as it fell into a puddle, saw the glowing red arc it described as it flew through the night. Mark started the engine, stared ahead as it idled.

'I must be stupid to let you go,' he said heavily. 'If I hadn't said anything we'd be making love by now.'

She caught the quick hard look he gave her, felt the searching insistence of the blue eyes.

'Lie about that,' Mark said through his teeth. 'You were giving me everything I wanted. Why?'

She didn't answer; she couldn't answer. The truth was far too dangerous, and she would not lie to him about that. Although she was deeply glad that he had halted the progress of that runaway lovemaking she felt a piercing regret at the same time because now she knew how badly she wanted, needed, Mark's passion and she knew she could not ever have it.

'Why?' he repeated insistently, his voice harsh. 'Are you frustrated. Helen? Doesn't he come home to you at night? Why do you sleep alone in that chaste little room of yours if you still want him?'

'Please,' she said tremblingly, 'take me home.'

'Home?' He laughed on a savage note. 'What a word for that empty shell of a house! I could smell the silence and loneliness the minute I walked into it. Helen, I could beat you!' But he started the car and drove the rest of the way without another word. Helen whispered goodnight and dived from the car into the house, hearing him drive away as she closed the door. The silence and loneliness Mark had mentioned came flooding round her as she stood there in the small hallway. She felt it as tangibly as the clammy touch of rain. Outside the night beat invisibly on the walls and roof and Helen stood without moving, an ache growing deep inside her body.

She was nervous when she went into work next day, but Mark's manner had returned to the quiet courtesy which made it possible for them to work together without strain. She was grateful for that, and behind her gratitude, even more conscious of the strength of character which made her love him. Mark's capacity for self-control was a daily revelation to her. She saw him in difficult situations all the time, his manner rarely varying, coping with insolence, rage, indifference without losing his temper.

When they made love in his car it had been Mark who had broken the burning chain binding them together. She would never have done it; it disturbed her to admit that. She had been lost to all self-awareness, swamped by desire. Mark had been as deeply aroused as she had—she knew that, had felt the hunger in his body as he kissed and touched her—but nevertheless it had been Mark who had stopped it, and Helen's admiration for him fed on that as it fed on all the other small evidence she gleaned from watching him. His strength came from an inner certainty. Helen loved it. Paul, in a similar situation, would have avidly taken whatever he could get. Mark had drawn back, not because he did not want what Helen was offering him, but because he was capable, even at that moment, of thinking for her, seeing ahead and refusing to take advantage of her temporary loss of control.

Paul returned from Tokyo and to her surprise had brought her a present, a small Japanese fan, exquisitely painted on fine silk with a handle of delicately carved bone. Helen's pleasure was genuine, her smile for once warm again.

He was amazed and delighted with her redecoration of his room. They stood in the doorway together while he stared around and exclaimed,

'That was quick! I like the new curtains. How long did it take you?'

The conversation got them over the difficulty of seeing each other again. Paul stayed at home that evening and talked excitedly about Japan, fascinated by everything he had seen, eager to talk about it, and Helen listened, smiling. At one point he asked casually, 'What have you been up to? Apart from decorating my room?'

'Working,' she said lightly.

Paul gave a short laugh. 'You're one of a kind, Helen. They don't make them like you any more.' He sounded bitter, resentful, and she met his eyes with a thrust of alarm, but he pushed the moment away and talked about Japan again, boasting of the success he had had on his trip.

It seemed he had been successful; Mark was very pleased with the order book he brought back. Paul came out of Mark's office and gave Helen a kiss as he passed, stooping to press it on her surprised mouth before he swung away. The door closed behind him and she stared at it. A movement surprised her. Looking round, she found Mark watching her with a harsh, cold face. Flushing, she bent over her work.

That evening Paul did not come home. Helen went to bed at ten and fell asleep almost at once. She was woken from a deep, dream-filled sleep to find herself being shaken violently. Looking up in dazed confusion, she found Paul bending over her, his face darkly flushed, his eyes glittering.

'You lying little bitch!'

She struggled to sit up and he pushed her back against her pillows, kneeling on the bed, his tie half off, his breath thick with whisky. 'He's had you, hasn't he? Hasn't he?'

The cruel hands went from her shoulders to her throat, clutching and choking her. She put her own hands up to pull them away and they tightened until she could scarcely breathe.

'Paul, don't!' she gasped.

'Don't?' He laughed, his lips curling back from his teeth. 'I told you what I'd do if you let him lay a hand on you.' The bright eyes flicked down her body and she heard the intake of his breath. 'Yes,' he said in that thick voice. 'If he can, I can.'

Sickness rose inside her. She couldn't bear it if he touched her like that, if he made her give in to him. She summoned all her courage and asked icily, 'What are you talking about? How dare you burst in here in the middle of the night and attack me?'

'Attack you? I haven't even started on you yet. When I've finished with you, you won't be using that highhanded tone with me.' Paul's face had an excited cruelty, his eyes as sharp as steel. 'And don't lie to me. I know, Helen.'

'What do you know?' She watched, tense, puzzled.

'He took you to dinner with his family the other night and drove you home afterwards.' Paul's eyes flared with a violence which terrified her. 'And he didn't get back until three in the morning, you little bitch!'

The words took Helen by such surprise that she gasped. Paul glared at her, his eyes hard.

'So don't try to lie to me—I know. He came in, didn't he? I gave the pair of you a perfect opportunity. We don't need any prizes for guessing what

took so long, do we? Was it in here? Or did you
use my bed? More room for the fun and games in
there.'

Helen was white to the lips. 'He dropped me at
the front door and went,' she said thinly, her voice
shaking. Jealousy was piercing her with a burning
pain. Where had Mark gone? He had been aroused,
sexually excited, so had he gone looking for someone more accessible? Who? Her eyes flickered
with a jealousy she could not hide. 'He didn't spend
those hours with me,' she said hoarsely.

Paul knelt there, his body tense, staring at her.
'You're lying,' he said, but his tone lacked convic-
tion and there was sharp watchfulness in his eyes.

'He didn't,' Helen told him, so angry with Mark
that somehow her voice lashed like a cold wind. 'He
was not with me.'

Paul's eyes narrowed. 'But you wish he had been,'
he said slowly. 'My God, you're jealous!'

'No!' She was trembling violently, staring at him.

'Sick with it,' Paul growled in sudden barbed
fury. 'I can see it in your face. Did you want him,
Helen? Didn't he want you? Or did he make a
pass and get slapped down so went to get it elsewhere?' He was watching her shrewdly and now he
smiled unpleasantly. 'Yes, that's it, isn't it? You
sent him away, but you wanted him.'

'I don't want anyone,' Helen said with bitter
finality. 'Men make me sick—all of them!' At that
moment she meant it, every word, her voice harsh
and icy, and Paul looked at her and read the con-
viction in her voice and face.

'So long as you don't want him,' he said slowly.

Helen put her hands to his wrists and dragged

his hands away from their painful clutch on her throat. 'Can I get to sleep now?' She was aching to be alone, to let the agony wash over her. Mark had gone to someone else that night. She had lain alone in her cold bed shivering with love and desire while he was with someone else. No wonder he had been calm and polite in the office next day! The miraculous self-control she had admired so much had come from a man who had satisfied the needs she had felt rising in him. He hadn't been aching with frustration, like her.

'Maybe I have other ideas,' Paul said with a return of his excited anger. His eyes moved greedily over the smooth pale shoulders, the white lace which left her warm white breasts half revealed. 'You're too lovely to sleep alone, Helen. And you're my wife.' His hand reached out and she tried to evade the movement. His fingers curled fiercely around one of her breasts, freeing it from the nightdress.

'Don't!' she cried, sickness boiling inside her.

Paul cupped it, turning the small hard nipple up towards him, and Helen saw his satisfied smile. She might loathe him, but she could not hide the hardened flesh which told him she was sexually aroused. That it had no connection with him was something he must not know. Her body was aching for Mark, but Paul was unaware of that.

'And you want me,' Paul said thickly, laughing. 'Don't pretend, Helen.' His golden head bent. His mouth opened around the dark circle which was pulsing with blood. Helen moaned in shock and repulsion and Paul took it for a cry of pleasure. His

hands covered her body, his head moved languidly,
enjoyment in the movements.

Helen struggled to think. She had to stop him,
but she knew that physically she was helpless. He
was lying across her now, pressing her down on the
bed. How had he found out about Mark driving
her home and coming back at three in the morning? Her body stiffened.

'How did you know?' she asked, pushing his head
back.

He raised an excited, flushed face. 'Stop trying to
talk your way out of it, Helen. Lie back and enjoy
it.'

'Who told you?' She stared at him. 'Joanne?'

The question changed the aroused look in his
face to a shifting uneasiness. He frowned and his
mouth took on a petulant irritation. 'A little bird
told me. Does it matter? I know, that's all.'

'Are you seeing Joanne?'

'Of course not,' he said, and she knew at once
that he lied. His face had that restless look, his eyes
not meeting her own.

'Who else would tell you? Paul, what do you
think you're doing? She's a child. How can you do
it? What is going on between you? Where do you
meet her? What's happened? How far has it gone?'
The questions burst out of her in rapid succession
and Paul sat up, grating his teeth, his face angry
and sullen, trying to interrupt her several times,
only to have her sweep on with a new question.

'Nothing's going on,' he said when she finished
talking at last. 'What are you talking about? All
right, it was Joanne who told me. I just bumped
into her at the club.'

'Is that where you meet her?'

'I don't meet her,' he said, lying again.

'It's got to stop,' Helen broke out angrily.

He gave her a quick, half-smiling look, a pleased little glint in his eyes. 'Jealous?'

'Disgusted,' she bit out, and his smile went.

'You're lying,' he said. 'You're jealous right enough. Your eyes are full of it.'

'If you must have other women find someone who won't get hurt,' she said bitterly. 'Leave that child alone.'

'O.K.,' he murmured. 'Be nice to me and I will.'

For a few seconds it hung in the air between them. Helen shuddered. He stared at her, waiting.

'No,' she whispered. He didn't even mean that. He had come here from being with Joanne and if she let him make love to her now he would be back with Joanne within a few days. She had no illusions about him at all. He was incapable of meaning any-thing, keeping any promise. He promised anything to get what he wanted at the moment.

To distract him she asked. 'How long have you been seeing her? How far has it gone?'

'Find out,' Paul said viciously, getting up. 'The kid's crazy about me. I wouldn't have to go on my knees to get her.'

'Mark Eliot will kill you,' Helen said furiously.

Paul laughed. 'I'm not scared of him.' But he was, she saw it in his eyes, and it gave her hope. Would Paul have gone far with Joanne knowing what reaction he would get from Mark if and when he found out?

'You will be when he finds out you've been see-ing her,' she told him. 'You aren't dealing with a

woman this time. Mark Eliot will leave marks on
you that will teach you a lesson you won't forget.'

'Oh, you'd like that, wouldn't you?' He turned
on her, angry because she had alarmed him. 'You
wouldn't be thinking of dropping him a hint,
would you, Helen? Because if you do, I'll make you
sorry you were ever born!'

'What makes you think I'm not now?'

He drew in his lower lip at the icy question.
'You're still my wife. You owe more loyalty to me
than to Eliot, and don't forget it.'

'You've traded on my loyalty enough. Either you
keep away from that child or I tell her brother.'

Paul's face worked furiously. 'I ought to take a
belt to you! Maybe that would teach you a few
lessons.'

'You've taught me enough lessons in the past. I
don't need any more.'

'You're frigid,' he burst out. 'No wonder Eliot
looked elsewhere—I don't blame him!'

He slammed out of the room and Helen lay
there, gnawing her lower lip, her eyes fixed in burning misery. Paul had told her weeks ago that Mark
had a name for womanising and she hadn't believed him. She had forgotten it in the past weeks.
Now she remembered, and she hated him.

She pushed aside her own feelings. What was
she going to do about Joanne? She could not just
ignore the situation, let it go on until the child was
forced to face some terrible problem. Paul would
seduce her, desert her when he was bored. Joanne
was drifting blindly into a disaster and Helen
could not stand aside and watch it happen without
trying to do something to stop it.

She could not rely on Paul's word. Even if she got him to promise never to see the girl again, he would not necessarily keep it. He would merely hide it better, cover up in some way. Paul had as much fixity of purpose as an amoeba or jellyfish, he floated aimlessly in the warm seas of his own selfish whim.

His attempt to sleep with her tonight had told her something. Paul might be pursuing Joanne, but he had not yet slept with her, Helen suspected. Joanne was a sweet, vulnerable child and no doubt her conscience was bothering her. Why had she told Paul about Mark coming home so late? Had Joanne, too, suspected that Mark had spent those hours with Helen? And would that belief make Joanne feel justified in taking the last step in her relationship with Paul? Helen knew Paul too well not to guess that he had been trying to talk the girl into bed. Maybe now he might succeed if Helen did not stop it.

I'll ring her, Helen decided, switching out the light. I must talk to her, get her to see what sort of mess she'll be getting into if she goes on seeing Paul.

CHAPTER SEVEN

SHE did not have to ring Joanne; the girl came into the office with Mark next morning. She gave Helen a brief, nervous little smile which did not quite hide the peculiar look in her eyes as they glanced at Helen. Mark said cheerfully, 'Hang on, Jo, I'll get the money from the safe.'

He strode into his office and the door slammed. Helen said quickly: 'I've got to see you, Joanne. I want to talk to you.'

Joanne turned her dark head and an insolence came into her face. She looked at Helen, smiling. 'What about? Or can I guess?' She glanced at her brother's closed door, still smiling.

Helen flinched. The alteration in Joanne's manner was marked and not pleasant. Helen could see exactly what the girl thought.

'Can we meet for lunch today?' she asked, all the same.

Joanne shrugged her slender shoulder. 'If you like.'

The door opened and Mark strode back into the room with an envelope which he handed to his sister. 'Now, be careful. It's a lot of money to be carrying around. Go easy.'

'Don't fret,' Joanne said casually. She looked at Helen. 'What time?'

Mark's face grew puzzled. He glanced from one to the other.

'Twelve-thirty,' said Helen, not meeting his eyes. 'At the Swan.'

Joanne nodded and went out of the room. Mark pushed his hands into his pockets, rocking on his heels. 'Meeting Joanne for lunch?'

'Yes.' Helen slid a new sheet of paper into the typewriter and Mark watched her.

'Why?'

She caught the curiosity and tension in his voice. Mark was suspicious. 'Why not? Your sister is a very nice girl.'

He relaxed. 'Isn't she? She's been a little difficult lately. My mother tends to try to run her life more than Joanne likes, and there've been some bad rows. I'd like her to make friends with you, Helen.'

The gentleness in his voice merely made her stiffen. She didn't look at him, but began to type. Mark watched her and she felt him trying to pierce the cool mask of her face, but she didn't look round at him. In the end he went into his office and she went on typing.

At a quarter past twelve she stopped work and began to get ready to go to lunch. When the door opened she glanced round hoping it was not a problem which would delay her, but it was Sara Compton. She was wearing a very chic little jacket over a tight black skirt, her bronze curls newly styled into a feathery frame for her pretty face.

A frown crossed her smooth forehead. 'Oh, I'd forgotten you work here now.' The realisation clearly did not delight her.

Helen gave her a polite smile. 'Did you want Mr Eliot?'

'Yes.' Sara used a cool, snubbing voice. 'Tell him I'm here, will you?'

Helen never needed to—the door to his office was flung open and he smiled at Sara. 'I thought I heard your voice.'

She swung towards him, smiling seductively, the trim little body moving into his arms. 'Darling, take me to lunch.'

Mark dropped a kiss on her nose. 'What an irresistible invitation!' Helen watched the blue eyes teasing the girl and her stomach whirled in sick understanding. She had imagined that Sara was Robby's girl—they were of an age and they had looked right together, but the fluttering eyelashes and pouting smile told her that Sara was far more interested in Mark.

Helen abruptly walked out, closing the door very quietly. Was that where he had gone when he left her? Jealousy stung and burnt inside her, but she whipped herself back into line. She had no right to feel like that, none whatever. She refused to let emotions to which she had no right take hold of her.

Mark was free and an adult; he could do just as he pleased. Helen despised herself for the unbidden reactions which had risen up inside her as she watched his arms go round the other girl.

She walked to the Swan and found Joanne irritably looking at her watch. The change in the girl since the first time they met struck Helen forcibly. The shy sweetness she had first glimpsed in that little face had become a harder, more confident look. Paul was having his usual effect, Helen thought bitterly. He was devastating to young girls and his reaction on them was incalculable.

'Oh, there you are. I was just going.' Joanne talked coldly, her face insolent.

'I'm sorry, I got held up. Shall we go in?'

The lunch was solid and unimaginative but well cooked, and they were able to get a table far enough away from eavesdroppers to talk without too much constraint.

Helen glanced at Joanne hesitantly as she began. 'I want first of all to say that you were wrong in imagining that your brother was with me the other night until three in the morning.'

Joanne flushed and tilted her head. 'Really?' Her tone said that she didn't believe it.

'Really,' Helen said in a firm, cold voice. 'Ask him if you don't believe me. I don't know where he was, but he dropped me at my home and he did not come into the house.'

Joanne's insolence fell away. She looked uncertainly at Helen, unable to refute the cool clear tone in which Helen spoke.

'But don't allow your suspicion about that to make you think that you can have a clear conscience about Paul.'

Helen's carefully delivered sentence made all Joanne's colour rush away and then come back in a hot flood.

'I ... what do you mean? I don't know what you're talking about.'

Helen could almost have smiled at the shaking, frightened little voice, the guilt and fear in the great blue eyes. Innocence still lay in them, a child's remorse and anxiety.

Helen smiled gently after a long moment. 'It hasn't gone too far yet, then?'

Joanne wriggled like a schoolgirl, looking around her in horror. 'I don't know what you're talking about.'

'I'm not angry,' Helen said, looking directly at her. 'Believe me, I'm not angry with you. It isn't the first time and it won't be the last.'

Joanne's eyes rounded and grew glazed with shock.

'Let me tell you about my husband,' Helen said with a sigh. Joanne opened her mouth and Helen said quickly, 'Listen to me. If when I've told you you still want to go on seeing him, I can't stop you. I may despise you as a fool, but I won't try to stop you. I'm telling you this now because I like you and I'd hate to see you getting yourself into a miserable state over a man like my husband.'

'You don't love him,' Joanne broke out huskily, accusing her with those big blue eyes.

Helen laughed. 'Love him? No, Joanne, I don't love him. To love Paul you would have to be an innocent like you, and although I was once young and blind enough to be taken in, I've grown out of my stupidity. Paul killed the feelings I had for him once.' She began to tell Joanne the whole story, sparing her nothing, and although at first the girl looked incredulous and angry, gradually her face paled and her eyes took on a numb dismay which told Helen that her story was being believed.

'Ask your brother, if you don't believe me,' Helen said in the end. 'He knows my husband. Ask how many jobs Paul has had—how many times we've had to move to get away from the scandal he creates.'

'Why haven't you divorced him?' Joanne demanded in a shaking voice which still held a residue of doubt.

'I ask myself the same question. I don't know. I don't believe in divorce except as a last resort and I haven't yet got the courage to admit how hopelessly I've failed,' Helen said bitterly.

'Of course, it couldn't be your fault,' Joanne accused, her blue eyes bright, glistening with unshed tears.

'Do you think I don't ask myself that too? Of course, part of it must be—there are always two sides to every problem. Paul and I were never suited and I should never have married him, but the fact remains that my husband is not a very nice man.'

Joanne's lips were quivering like a child's. 'I love him,' she said huskily.

Their eyes held in a wordless knowledge. 'I'm sorry,' Helen said very gently. 'I am sorry. I know it's hard for you to face it, but in the long run you'll suffer less if you break it off now.'

'How do I know you aren't just lying to make me give him up?' the girl burst out.

'You don't,' Helen admitted wryly. 'Of course I could be—but I'm not.' She paused. 'He's tried to persuade you to go to bed with him, of course.'

Joanne didn't meet her eyes or answer. Helen smiled drily. 'I imagined he must have. Did he try again after you'd told him what you suspected of me and your brother?'

Joanne still didn't answer, but her lashes flickered nervously, giving Helen the answer she expected.

'Does he say he loves you?'

Joanne whispered shakily, 'Please, don't talk about it.'

'I must,' Helen said in a firm voice. 'He does say he loves you, doesn't he? Yet last night he came back to me and tried to force me to give him what you wouldn't.'

She heard Joanne's intake of breath, the sharp reflex jerk of pain the child gave. 'No,' Joanne muttered in anguish. 'I don't believe you!'

'Look at me,' Helen said gently.

Slowly Joanne lifted her head. The wide tear-filled blue eyes looked into Helen's and then closed in a silent misery.

'I'm sorry,' Helen said again. 'I didn't; and I can tell you now that it would make me sick to death to have to—almost as sick as it would make me to know that he'd talked you into it. I'm past hope, but you're so young. I'd hate to see him ruin your life too.'

She saw from Joanne's white face that she had won her argument. They parted in silence. Joanne walked away stiffly like someone who has a pain deep inside their body, and Helen sighed, watching her. She felt she had stabbed something small and innocent and helpless. What other choice had she had?

When she got back to the office there was no sign of Mark. He did not come back from his lunch with Sara Compton for another hour and when he did come into the office he was whistling, a smile on his face. He had enjoyed his lunch, Helen thought savagely. Wasn't he lucky?

Mark passed, paused and looked down at her averted head. 'Enjoy your lunch with Joanne?'

Helen almost laughed aloud. Enjoy that bitter, painful experience? She struggled to pull a mask over her face and slowly turned to look up at him, her eyes somehow managing to be cool.

'Very much.'

'Good.' He studied her, a frown knitting his dark brows. 'You're pale. Are you feeling well?'

'I've got a cold,' she lied.

'Oh? I hadn't noticed.'

'It's just starting,' she said. 'I've got a headache and I feel stuffy.'

'Take some aspirins,' said Mark, still frowning. 'Look, you get off home now and go to bed. You can't work if you're feeling ill.'

His kind concern made her sick. She jerked her head away. 'I'm all right.'

'Don't be absurd,' he said impatiently, his voice hardening. He took hold of her arm lightly. 'Come along, Helen.'

'Don't touch me!' she burst out, and his hand fell away. He stared at her, his eyes very dark.

'I'm sorry, I'd forgotten you were untouchable.' He spoke with a bite as harsh as her own. 'All the same, I won't have you working when you aren't up to par. Get your things and go home. That's an order, Helen.'

She stood up. 'Very well.'

'I'll drive you home,' he said.

'No,' she said thinly. 'I'll get a bus.'

'You'll do what you're told.' Mark was furious now, his face set in inexorable lines. The blue eyes had a kindled rage in them which flared out at her as he turned away.

He drove her home and as she turned to get out of the car said in a low voice, 'Stop punishing me.'

Helen froze. What did he mean? She half turned, feeling cold. 'For what?' For going to someone else the other night? she thought. He couldn't mean that. What did he mean?

'For making you feel things you didn't want to feel,' Mark said rapidly, huskily. 'I'm not being put through a mill because you hate to remember that you wanted me.'

'I'm not doing anything of the kind!'

'No?' He tapped his long fingers on the wheel with an impatience he did not bother to try to hide. 'I think you are. Do you think I can't feel what's going on inside that head of yours? He came home and you felt guilty, although God knows why you should, after all you've taken from him. So you came into work today and looked at me as if I were an enemy. I won't have it, Helen. Don't make me the scapegoat for your own remorse.'

She stared at his profile, seeing the clear hard features with a painful intensity. He had picked up her anger and misread it. A bitter little smile touched her face.

'You're wrong,' she said, opening the door. 'I don't blame you for anything.'

As she walked up to the front door she heard his car door slam and looked back, surprised and shaken to see him coming after her.

She threw a nervous glance along the other

houses. Someone was bound to have noticed his car, recognised him, begun to stare in fascinated curiosity. 'Please, go away,' she whispered as he joined her.

'Not yet,' Mark said tersely, and pushed her into the house. He shut the door and the tomblike silence enfolded them both. Mark cocked his head and listened to it, his face dry.

'How can you bear to stay?'

She walked away and stood in the chill little sitting-room, her head bent. 'We've got nothing to talk about.'

'What's wrong, Helen?' he demanded, ignoring her. 'Why have I been getting icy looks from you all day?'

'You haven't.'

'Don't lie to me! I can feel it.' He took a step and she heard him breathing behind her, the irregular quick breathing of a man under strain. 'I can feel it now. There's a wall between us, and it wasn't there before. Why is it there now?'

'You're imagining it.'

'I'm imagining nothing! It's there all right. Why? It wasn't there yesterday. When you arrived you gave me a nervous little smile, but there wasn't a damned great wall of ice between us. Now there is—why?'

She did not answer and he took hold of her shoulder. Helen could not bear the thrust of pleasure that contact sent through her. She turned on him, her eyes flashing. 'Don't touch me!'

The vibrations of his anger mounted. The blue eyes were dark and narrowed. His hands clamped down on her arms and held her.

Helen tried to pull free, trembling, staring up at him with heat coming into her throat at the look in his face. 'I'm not available, Mr Eliot, so leave me alone. Go somewhere else for what you seem to want.' She paused and her jealousy pierced like an agony beyond bearing. Huskily she added, 'Go wherever you went the other night. You won't get anything from me.'

He gave a sharp little exclamation, staring at her. 'What?'

She was regretting her outburst already and she turned her head away without answering.

'What are you talking abou?' Mark demanded, one hand lifting to her chin and turning her face towards his probing eyes.

'Please leave,' she muttered desperately, her eyes sliding away from his stare.

'You can't make accusations like that and not explain what you mean. Where I went the other night? What night?' A pause and he said slowly, 'Do you mean the night you had dinner with us?' She felt him watching her closely. 'You do. Where do you think I went?'

'I don't care!' Pain was eating at her like acid and it came out in her voice.

'Helen,' he said in a shaken voice, 'do you want to know where I was after I left you? I walked for hours in the rain like a lovesick schoolboy. Do you think I was in any state to go calmly home to bed? Don't you know anything about men? I was in no mood to sleep.' He paused and added deeply, 'Or to go elsewhere, Helen. I'm not your husband—I couldn't just shove off and find someone else.'

Sick relief flooded into her. She had suffered appallingly while she believed that Mark was no better than Paul. Her whole body began to tremble and Mark put his arms around her to stop the convulsive shaking.

'You were jealous,' he whispered into her hair.

She could not move, could not speak, her eyes closed and her heart thudding heavily as she felt his face moving against her hair. Suddenly it lifted. He looked down at her and Helen opened her eyes dazedly to look back at him.

'How did you know I didn't get home until the early hours?' His frown was thoughtful.

She flushed, biting her lip.

'Joanne,' he guessed with a grimace.

There was no point in lying. Only a member of his family could have told her. 'She heard you come home,' Helen admitted.

'And the row.' Mark's face was sardonic.

'Row?' Helen stared at him.

'My mother waited up for me,' he said drily. 'In the best traditions of the family.'

'Oh!' exclaimed Helen, horrified.

'It wasn't very pleasant,' he sighed. 'We had quite a scene.'

'She thought ...' Helen began in shock, flushing again.

'Oh, she thought, all right,' Mark said flatly. 'My mother has a nasty tongue. I got a lecture on the sanctity of marriage which went on for a long time.'

Helen shivered, moving away from him. 'I can't blame her. She's right.'

'She knows nothing about it, and I told her so.' Mark's voice had a snap like a whip. 'My father was no Eastwood. I can't see my mother putting up with it the way you do.' His eyes moved away and he frowned. 'How did you come to discuss it with Joanne?' The clever face toughened. 'Don't tell me that was why you had lunch with her? She wasn't having the insolence to interfere, was she?'

'No, no,' she said quickly, seeing the anger in his face and not wishing to bring that down on Joanne's head.

'Why did you have lunch with her?' Mark watched her, his eyes piercing and far too intelligent.

Helen hesitated, unsure what to say. Mark drew a sharp breath. 'She hasn't been seeing Easwood again?'

Helen was aghast at his quickness and he read her look of shock. 'My God,' he burst out harshly, 'the stupid little fool! What's been going on?' His eyes were leaping, his face dark with hot colour. 'Were you warning her off, Helen? Another attempt to save your marriage?'

She suddenly felt the tension in him and recognised it. Mark was jealous. Her eyes widened, a sad little smile in them. 'No,' she said flatly. 'I was trying to stop Joanne making a fatal mistake as I did.'

Mark's face changed. He touched her cheek. 'How did you find out about them?'

'Joanne told Paul that you hadn't come back until three after driving me home,' Helen admitted. 'He was so angry he forgot what he was saying and I realised how he'd found out.'

'Eastwood believes I was with you?' Mark looked at her searchingly.

'I told him you weren't.'

He watched her, his blue eyes almost black. 'What happened?'

She flushed. 'He believed me.'

'What did you have to do to make him believe it?'

His voice had such a thick bitterness that she stared at him and her own voice shook as she said, 'No, Mark. No, I didn't.' And as she said it she knew that in her own mind if she let Paul touch her she would be committing a betrayal of Mark which would sear her. The realisation went through her like a knife. She whitened and shook, and Mark's arms went round her, pulling her against him, holding her possessively.

'I couldn't stand it,' he muttered into her hair.

'Don't, Mark.' She was crying now, silently, because the pain of loving without hope was more than she could stand. She pushed him away and he straightened, a lean tense dangerous figure, the blue eyes looking at her demandingly.

'Leave him. Come to me.'

'I can't!'

For a moment the silent struggle raged between them, his face taut with anger.

She broke off, turning away. 'Don't worry about Joanne. I've made her see what sort of man Paul is —I'm sure it will stop now.'

'Oh, I'll make sure of that,' Mark said heavily. 'I'll send her away. She can go to London. We have an aunt there who'll keep an eye on her.'

He moved to the door. 'Will you be all right on your own?'

'Yes.' It cost a lot to utter even that monosyllable. The cry of need and pain she wasn't uttering hovered on her lips and never emerged. She looked at the tall figure, the dark head, and anguish burnt in her eyes.

When he had gone she couldn't even cry; the pain was too bad even for tears. She just sat and looked at the wall, hearing the cry of the wind along the street as if it were inside herself.

She was wildly glad to know that Mark had not gone to someone else that night. It had eased her jealousy, but it had made her see that her jealousy had somehow deepened her feelings for him, widening and intensifying it, driving a great hole into her firm intention of forgetting him. The pain she suffered had fertilised her feelings, making them spring thicker and stronger. She had been faced with a jealousy more profound than any she had ever felt for Paul, and the agony of that jealousy had been a revelation to her.

She thought of Mark walking in the wind and rain, with the great empty moors around him, and closed her eyes in an access of terrible joy. Mark had been walking to force down the emotions they had shared in his car. She had not been the only one to struggle like a limed bird against the helpless, unslaked passion which had suddenly caught them both that night.

I've got to stop seeing him, she thought in a sick realisation. This can't go on, I can't let it. While she was working with him day after day the feelings would get stronger. Already she was floundering like someone with their feet in a bog and if she went on seeing him she would find it harder and harder to deny what they both ached for so badly.

I've got to resign. She said it aloud as though speaking the words would give her the strength to do it.

The empty house echoed them back to her like a mocking refrain. If only I'd never met Paul, never married him. I would be free. She got up abruptly. She could not let herself play that futile, stupid game of makebelieve. Things were what they were, one had to accept life as it came, one could not throw away reality.

She would give in her notice on Monday, she decided. Having made up her mind she felt a faint relaxation of the stress she was under and she was able to push all thoughts of Mark out of her head as she went upstairs.

All her good intentions came to nothing in the end. That Saturday Paul went out and bought himself a gleaming new car, an expensive model which would take them a year to pay for, but which put Paul into a very good mood for the rest of the weekend. He insisted on taking her for a drive in it that Sunday. The shiny new toy obsessed him. He hummed as he drove around the moors, his face as happy as that of a child with a toy car. He's a child, Helen thought, watching him—a vain, careless, selfish and handsome child who'll never grow up.

'Beautiful, isn't she, Helen?' He gave her a vivid smile, his eyes very bright.

'Beautiful,' she agreed. And if they were to manage to pay for it, she could not give up her job, because they could never keep up the hire purchase payments on Paul's salary alone.

He let the speed creep up, laughing under his breath as they tore across the great brown crests of the hills above the town. The rain had vanished. The sun shone in watery illumination and the valleys below took on a misty brightness which made them distant and beautiful.

They visited a market town some fifteen miles from Ryethorpe. Helen did some sightseeing in the twelfth-century church while Paul went off to have a drink alone. There were some faded brass plates let into the cold grey stone floors, and Helen watched a woman in jeans rubbing away at them, her head bent in absorption. The high altar was lit with wintry sunshine and the scent of chrysanthemums gave a smoky sweetness to the clammy air inside the stone walls. Helen sat down and just enjoyed the silence and peace. Above her on the walls hung tattered regimental banners where some Victorian soldiers had been buried long ago with pomp and ceremony. Their white marble figures leaned on a white marble cannon with as much elegance as though they were about to go to a ball. So sad and so senseless, she thought, looking at them.

She was to meet Paul back at the car. As she walked slowly into the market square she saw him standing on the other side of it, smiling with all his charm down at a slim young woman with short red curls. Helen paused, wryly watching them. Paul looked across at her and Helen walked onwards. When she reached him he was alone again, and there was a malicious innocence in his handsome face.

He put her into the car with exaggerated gallantry. As he got in beside her his eyes slid away and Helen caught sight of the redheaded girl again. They drove past her and Paul gave her a quick half-hidden smile. Helen knew him too well not to read meaning into the look the two of them exchanged. Paul had made some sort of arrangement with the girl; it was in his face as he looked sideways at her a moment later. Helen looked at him blankly, indifferently. There had been none of Joanne's vulnerable innocence in the other girl's flirtatious eyes. She could look after herself.

CHAPTER EIGHT

THE autumn finally gave way to winter and surprisingly the weather turned, too, giving way to cool bright days when the sun shone gently without overmuch heat and the moors took on a stark beauty which the wind cried over like a curlew. Helen was finding it easier now to bear her constant proximity to Mark. He made it easy for her, she recognised. They kept an invisible barrier between them every time they were alone, their voices, faces, calm and polite. He never put a foot over the line he had drawn for himself. Helen was grateful for the thought he showed in preserving their distance.

Joanne had gone to London, as Mark had promised, and Paul was bitingly malicious about that. 'Did you tell him, after all? What did he have to say? He hasn't said a word to me.' The empty shallow eyes held spite. 'But he looks at me as if he'd like to pound me into fragments.'

Helen ignored it, placing his breakfast in front of him. Although she now worked long hours too, Paul of course expected her to run the house, do the cooking, have his shirts clean when he wanted a new one. Paul took such services for granted. Women were put into the world to care for a man's needs—his mother had taught him that, and Paul believed it implicitly. Helen might keep him out of her bed, but she wasn't going to default on any other service to him.

Paul was too occupied with someone else to bother himself over her, though. He never came home in the evenings at all. Helen heard him come in late each night, sometimes sober, sometimes slightly drunk. She did not know who the other woman was—perhaps it was still the girl she had seen him with before. Helen preferred not to know. She was existing in a limbo for the moment where the only thing that mattered was getting through the endless days and nights without pain.

She felt like someone with a terminal disease who looked upon a day which only held a little pain as a day of triumph. Her feelings for Mark were anaesthetised, numbed, but always present below the surface.

At weekends she walked across the moors in an effort to tire her body into an unfeeling acceptance. She grew to know the terrain, recognising the shapes and relationships of each rolling sweep of land, watching the birds which floated like feathers in the pale blue sky.

Paul was spending more money than ever. He frequently borrowed from her at the end of the week, claiming he had heavy commitments. Helen knew what they were, but she said nothing, and handed over what he asked without comment. Having money kept him cheerful; lack of it made him sullen and nasty. It irked her that he should be spending her hard-earned money on another woman, but she would rather that than have Paul turn on her with that vicious, sullen face.

The hours she spent out on the moors were

peaceful, a haven after her anxieties and stresses at work and home. She loved the springy cushions of heather, the acid scent of the soil, the deep green carpet of grass which warned that the ground was swampy underfoot.

One Saturday, just before Christmas, she was walking in the empty brown landscape when she heard hooves and looked round in shock to see Mark galloping towards her. He drew rein and looked down at her, his eyes equally surprised.

'Hallo.'

'Hallo,' she said, stupidly shy.

He slid down from the broad back and looped the reins over his arm. 'Taking a walk?'

'Yes. It's a nice day.'

They were making conversation as though they barely knew each other, their voices and faces stiff and courteous.

'My mother told you the rain would stop one day,' he said, slightly teasing, a sidelong smile filled with charm that stopped her heart.

'I remember.' She had not seen his mother since that one evening. Helen suspected that Mrs Eliot did not approve of her or approve of the fact that she was Mark's secretary. He might have told his mother that there was nothing going on between them, but perhaps Mrs Eliot had picked up something in the air as they looked at each other.

He glanced across the rolling landscape. 'On a fine day this is one of the loveliest sights in the world.'

'It is,' she agreed, watching his profile with passion.

He turned his head before she could look away

and his eyes changed, a spark leaping into them.

'Helen,' he said hoarsely, dark red sweeping into his face.

She trembled. 'Don't,' she muttered, turning away.

He dropped the reins and the horse bent his long neck to graze on some grass growing among the heather, tearing at it with a rough movement.

'I can't go on like this,' Mark said thickly, moving closer to her, watching her. 'Don't you care that you're driving me insane?'

'Do you think it's easy for me?' She looked at him helplessly, her lips quivering. The wind blew a fine pale strand of hair free from her chignon and Mark suddenly put his hands to her head and freed all her hair so that it tumbled round her face in a wash of silver.

'So that's what you look like with it down,' he said broodingly, running his fingers through the silken fall of it, letting it blow away from his hand in a light banner. 'Do you know I dream of waking up to find you in my bed with your lovely hair streaming over my pillow?'

Helen's breath caught. She could not look away from him, her eyes filled with an intense and burning passion.

'What do you dream, Helen?' he asked, moving closer.

She looked at his mouth, heat throbbing inside her. It came nearer and with a weak groan she lifted her face for it. Mark gave a stifled sound of hunger, then his mouth searched and found hers, her lips opening like petals at the touch of the sun, burning, melting.

Her body was shuddering in his arms, her eyes closed, her hands moving over his back, the rough touch of his tweed jacket under her palms. She kissed him with a desperation she could not disguise and he deepened the kisses in a ruthless demand which bruised her soft lips and sent flame leaping along her veins.

Panic bubbled up inside her as she felt her own desire breaking loose. She pushed at his wide shoulders and stumbled away from him, beginning to run, only to catch her foot in a rabbit hole and trip, falling heavily face down in the heather.

Mark knelt beside her and turned her over gently, his arm sliding under her body. 'Hurt yourself?' The anxiety in his voice made her quiver with response. She shook her head, trying to get up.

Mark held her, one hand clamped round her shoulder, staring down at her. 'I'm in love with you,' he said deeply.

Helen closed her eyes, happiness lancing her body, and Mark lifted her slightly as he bent to find her mouth. Weakly she wound her arms round his neck and kissed him back, feeling the threatening desire ignite irresistibly inside her. Mark undid her coat and his long hands slid inside it. He slowly opened her shirt and caressingly cupped the warm swell of her breasts. Helen moaned, her lips clinging to his.

'Oh, my darling,' he muttered, 'I want you so badly.'

Feverishly she ran her hands down his long back, her body arched in excited response to the movements of his hands as they freed her breasts, discovered the sexual arousal they gave away. His dark head moved down to them and she lay in his arms, her dazed eyes watching the wheeling, empty sky while his lips played with her hardened nipples and his fingers stroked the smooth white flesh. Pleasure dominated her, a pleasure she had not felt for a long time. She ached for the final, necessary surrender, feeling Mark move restlessly against her, his thigh on hers.

Mark suddenly lifted his head, breathing raggedly. 'We can't go on like this,' he muttered huskily. 'You must leave him, Helen. You don't give a damn for him and I can't stand knowing you're living in that house alone with a man like that.'

Helen stared at the sky. Her stomach was clenched on an agony she could no longer stand. 'Yes,' she whispered dryly, 'I know.'

She felt the blue eyes burning on her. 'You'll leave him?'

She shifted restlessly. 'Give me time, Mark.'

'Time for what? You've had all the time in the world to find out what sort of swine he is—why do you even hesitate?'

'I've told you. Marriage is a rope that isn't easy to untie.'

'Don't linger over a high fence, Helen,' he said harshly. 'Just take it. It's the only way.'

'That depends on whether you think you can,' she said sadly.

Mark's breath was drawn sharply. 'Do you still love him?'

Helen shook her head.

'Are you sure?' Mark's voice had force and anger in it. 'You've let me make love to you, but I didn't hear you admitting you felt a thing for me.'

She felt her dry lips tighten. 'I can't,' she said miserably.

'Because you don't?' He sat up and pulled down his yellow sweater, brushed heather from his jacket, with the fixed absorption of someone doing anything to take his mind off what was occupying it. After a moment he asked brusquely, 'Were you using me to relieve frustration?'

'No,' she said unsteadily, hating the expression in his face.

'No?' He did not sound as if he believed that. 'What has he got? Do those looks of his still pull you, Helen? Are you waiting for him to turn back to you?'

'Do you think he doesn't?' Somehow the sneer in his voice made her angry and the question broke out of her furiously.

Mark's head came up and the blue eyes had a fierce, hard rage in them. 'So he does. You don't always sleep alone in that little nun's cell!'

She started to do up her shirt, her hands trembling. Mark got to his feet after a moment and walked away to get his horse. Helen stood up and turned away, sick with passion and misery. She did not want Mark to be angry with her. She did not want him to believe that she still let Paul make love to her. But she was torn in two by contrary impulses, the old obstinate feeling that she had to fight to keep her marriage intact warring with her passion for Mark.

Mark caught up with her, riding his horse again now. He drew rein and stared down at her bent head. Helen could not look at him, her toe pressing down the springy heather.

'Don't ever use me like that again,' he bit out harshly. 'Take out your frustrations on Eastwood. I've no doubt you can get him interested if you're as responsive with him as you were with me!'

Her face burning, she didn't answer, and after a moment Mark rode away, passing into a gallop which had fury in it, reminding her of the night she first saw him, when he had risen out of the wind like a storm god, his face and body stripped by the elements to the stark strength which she now saw as his basic quality. Mark was as enduring as the rock beneath the heather. He would age into the sort of beauty she had seen in his mother—a beauty of spirit which held courage and humanity. She felt sick after listening to his angry dismissal of her. It hurt deeply to know that he thought her wild response had been entirely fuelled by sexual frustration. She would have given anything to be free to answer his declaration of love with a declaration of her own. The words had burned on her tongue and she had bitten them back.

As she walked in the clean, strong landscape with the timeless endurance of the moors all round her, she ached to be able to go to Mark and tell him what she felt.

Faced with the actual problem of divorcing Paul, she always stumbled like a child in the dark, having no hand to guide her, no certainty to tell her she was acting wisely. She needed time. It was a leap into the unknown and her courage always failed her when she faced it. One part of her mind knew precisely what she wanted, how she felt. But there was that other, darker half of her mind which always put up a barrier, halting her. It was a mistake to act with a divided mind; she felt that deeply. Until the whole of her mind, conscious and subconscious, was ready to face the end of her marriage she would not try to end it. If she did, she was somehow sure she would move into the future with regret and pain like trailing filaments behind her.

It was so easy to judge from the outside. A situation always looks easy to those who are not trapped inside it. Mark did not, could not know, the pain of amputation. One had to be faced with the prospect of deciding to use the knife on one's own body before one could judge the hardship of the decision.

When she got back to the house Paul was not there. She had left him still in bed, sleeping thickly, heavily, after another late night. His room was empty now; clothes trailing everywhere, the bed rumpled and untidy, drawers and wardrobe gaping open. It was the usual scene of devastation Paul left behind him. Helen sighed and began to tidy everything back into place. She could guess where he had gone; there would be plenty of festive spirit in circulation at the country club just before Christmas. People would be moving into top gear for the season ahead, and Paul had plenty of money with him. He would be doing what he loved—showing off, making a splash, buying drinks and flattering every woman in sight, enjoying the power his golden looks gave him with them.

Karen Santen knocked at the door later in the afternoon and asked if she would babysit that evening. 'We want to go out for a drink,' she grinned. Helen promised she would and Karen gave her a grateful smile.

'You're marvellous! I don't know what we would do without you.'

Helen had fallen into the habit of babysitting for them once or twice a week. She enjoyed having care of Terry whose lively antics amused her and it was much more pleasant than sitting alone in her empty house watching the television hour after hour or reading a book. Even the most boring programme was better than listening to the silence beat on her ears. Sometimes she felt she ached for the sound of a human voice. She was marooned on a lonely island and Terry's company was always welcome to her.

Karen and her husband got back at eleven and after a brief chat, Helen went back to her own home and got ready for bed, where she slept badly, her body tormented by dreams of Mark. Somewhere towards dawn she was awoken by stumbling sounds on the stairs and then a crash. She ran out and found Paul lying on his face in the hall. Helen grimaced with anger and disgust. Drunk again, she thought, but as she reached him he stood up, shivering violently, his face deeply flushed and his eyes hectic.

'My head,' he muttered, putting a hand to it.

Silently she began to guide him up the stairs. Paul leaned on her heavily. 'I crashed the car,' he muttered.

'What?' She stopped, staring at him.

'Into a ditch,' he said in a thick intonation. 'I got out to dig the front wheels out and must have passed out. God knows how long I lay there. I came to and I was drenched.'

Helen had felt the dampness on his clothes. He was shivering, trembling, his features drawn.

'Paul! How can you ...' She stopped. What was the point of asking questions like that? He had been drunk and incapable.

'A chap stopped and helped me,' Paul said. 'Good of him. We got the car back on the road and I drove home. God knows how I got here—I felt worse and worse.'

'You look terrible,' said Helen, disturbed by something about him.

'It was damned cold lying there,' he said roughly. 'What do you expect?'

'I'll call a doctor,' she said as she helped him undress.

'No. I'll sleep it off,' Paul said irritably, pushing her away as she tried to get his pyjamas on. Naked, he fell into bed and dragged the covers over himself, turning on to his face as he always did. She looked at the sleek blond cap of hair and her eyes pricked with tears.

Turning out the light, she went downstairs and made herself some coffee. She sat in the kitchen watching the morning pale slowly outside.

At seven she crept into Paul's room and looked down at his half-visible face. Touching it with one finger, she winced at the heat burning in him. He had a temperature.

He stirred at her touch and his eyes flicked open. They were glazed and vague. 'Helen?' he mumbled thickly.

'How do you feel?' she asked anxiously.

'Terrible.' His lips were slow and barely moving.

'I'll get a doctor,' Helen said with anxiety.

Paul did not protest this time. He merely groaned and shut his eyes.

Helen rang the doctor and had difficulty in getting one who was prepared to come out on a Sunday. Eventually a small thin young Indian arrived and she explained what had happened. The young man took Paul's pulse and temperature expressionlessly, listened to his chest in intent silence.

Looking at Helen, he coiled his stethoscope. 'He is suffering slightly from the effects of exposure. I do not think it is serious—a little congestion in the chest and a high temperature, but they will pass if he stays in bed and takes care of himself.'

'I'll make sure he does,' she promised.

The doctor wrote out a prescription and gave her instructions on how to deal with Paul's condition, then left. Helen went back into the bedroom and Paul was asleep again, one arm flung over his hot face. He looked like a child, a cross, sick child, and she bent over him to fold his arm inside the sheet, brushing the rumpled hair back from his face.

She went next door to ask Karen to get the medicine which had been prescribed; the chemist would be open at eleven for an hour. Karen willingly agreed, asking about Paul's illness with concern. Terry begged Helen to stay and play and Helen smiled at her. 'Not today, darling. Uncle Paul is sick.'

'What's wrong with him?' Terry asked, and Helen almost laughed as the wider implications of the question sank into her mind.

'He has a bad cold,' she simplified.

'Give him my love,' Terry said with the wider

enthusiasm of childhood which sees no deeper than the golden mask.

Paul had a childish attitude to illness. He resented it and feared it. When his first long fevered sleep ended he became demanding, calling for cool drinks, a radio, newspapers. 'Stay with me, Helen,' he said sulkily as she was about to leave when he had run out of demands. 'I'm bored.'

Helen looked at him steadily. He was too ill for her to argue with him. She sat down on the edge of his bed and he fingered her arm, his lashes down, his mouth petulant.

'What have you got to do down there?' he asked resentfully. 'Talk to me.'

'What about?'

He shrugged. 'I don't know. Think of something.'

He sounded like a little boy crying: 'Tell me a story ...' He *was* a little boy, Helen thought, a spoilt and beautiful little boy who still held her trapped in a situation she found unbearable, the ties between them weakened but yet unbroken.

'My hair needs combing,' he said suddenly, running a hand over it. Helen brought a brush and supported his heavy head while she slowly restored the tossed strands to their usual smooth state. Paul lay there with closed eyes and a slight smile, an expression of enjoyment on his face.

He opened his eyes and the bright, still fevered eyes looked at her smilingly. 'Kiss me,' he whispered.

She hesitated, but only for a second. As she bent his arm came up round her neck and held her while he kissed her slowly but without passion.

'I need you, Helen,' he muttered against her mouth. 'Don't leave me.'

Her heart hurt. In a flash she saw the whole situation laid bare. She was Paul's only reality, his mother, his sister, his nurse. The other women were the toys that spoilt little boy coveted and chased, but he needed her to come home to because without her his world was insecure. She was his home, his safe retreat. Paul loved her in a way she had never suspected, did not really want. He loved her the way a child does love its mother—selfishly, fretfully, demandingly. Paul expected her to go on loving him as patiently and unchangingly as his mother had, and although he desired her body from time to time, it was this for which he really needed her, this safe and reliable love.

She had known this deep inside her for a long time, but she had never faced it until now, only known that some final string still held her to him, despite all he did. And it was this—the realisation that Paul did need her, that if she left him she would be abandoning him as surely as a mother abandons a child which cannot take care of itself.

She brushed his hair back from his hot forehead and kissed him there. 'I'm here,' she said huskily.

Paul sighed, leaning his head against her arm. With his eyes shut his face relapsed into a peaceful repose and all the small lines smoothed out, the spite and selfishness, the malice and sensuality, leaving it with a beauty which she had seen when they first met, the beauty which had caught at her heart.

They sat there in a wonderful silence, neither speaking, neither moving, and Helen wanted to cry but couldn't. Paul would never give her the love she needed, the protective adult love a man can give a woman, the love Mark offered her. She would go hungry all her life and Paul would never even know it.

But she could not leave him. Facing that was like facing death in the morning. Grim, inescapable, it haunted her as she sat there.

She saw suddenly that Paul had fallen asleep with the suddenness of the sick, his face still very hot, his lips twitching as though he mumbled silently.

Gently she laid his head down on the pillow and covered him, then tiptoed away, closing the door.

His mood did not last. When he woke up he was cross and irritable, fidgeting in the bed and complaining of everything she did. His head hurt, he said, and he needed a drink. His bed had crumbs in it, his sheets needed changing. 'Isn't there any ice?' He made a face over the lemon barley water she had brought him. 'Vile stuff! Helen, get me some ice, my throat hurts.'

She fought for patience, realising he was still ill. As night fell he calmed and grew sleepy again, asking her to sit with him while he dozed in a half sleep, holding her hand tightly, his fingers damp with sweat. She gently wiped his hands and face with a cool damp cloth and he sighed with pleasure. 'Thank you. That's good.'

She put down his hand when she thought he was asleep and began to move away. It groped for her. 'No, stay with me,' he muttered, a frown on his brow. 'Stay all night, Helen. Don't leave me alone.'

She bit her lip, staring at him. His eyes flicked

open. They pleaded and Helen slowly went back.

He clasped her in his arms, cuddling close to her back with a sigh of relief, his face hot against her bare shoulder. 'That's better,' he whispered. 'I hate sleeping alone.' There was no sensuality in the voice, only a heavy satisfaction.

Heley lay awake, listening to his breathing, feeling the restless movements of his overheated body behind her. His arms were round her waist, clasped lightly now but still holding her. She felt cold despite the heat emanating from him. Slowly she fell asleep. Several times Paul woke, once needing to go to the bathroom, once asking in a parched voice for water. Each time it took Helen longer to get back to sleep, but he fell back into it without a second's pause.

She woke up in the morning to see pale light trickling like water over the walls. Paul stirred as if she had inadvertently woken him. She felt him move, his breathing altering. His lips suddenly brushed her arm and then her shoulder. She stiffened and he turned her to face him. His skin was still flushed, but the overwhelming heat had lessened during the night. The bright blue eyes smiled at her. 'I feel better,' he said.

'Good,' said Helen, poised to go. 'I'll get you some breakfast.'

'I don't want breakfast,' he said, and stared at her. His hand stroked down her naked arm, trembling. 'Helen.'

She was poised on a knife edge, her flesh cringing from him, her mind knowing she had to do it. Paul stared, waiting. 'Helen, please,' he muttered.

She took a painful breath and let her body relax

against him. Her arms slowly went round his neck and Paul gave a satisfied sigh, bending to kiss her. His hands began to touch her, shaping her body, fondling it with the sensual enjoyment he had always shown. He burrowed his face between her breasts, groaning, 'You're so lovely. Don't be cold to me, Helen.'

Had it after all been mainly her fault? Had her rejection of his desire after he strayed for the second time been what had turned their marriage into a desert? If she had deliberately invited him, kept him too interested in her to look at anyone else, would things have gone differently? Helen did not know any more. She did not know anything. Sad, bewildered, she yielded herself to his hands and felt his excitement growing as he knew she was not going to reject him this time.

Helen fought down the instincts which struggled to stop him. She clamped an iron hand over her own feelings and hid from him the physical resistance she could not help. Holding his golden head between her hands, she kissed his mouth with an affection she disguised as passion, and Paul moaned softly with his eyes shut.

His trembling hands stroked her thighs. 'Love me, Helen,' he whispered thickly, and she allowed him to part them, the sickness inside her forced down.

A moment later Paul swore hoarsely and she looked at him in shock. 'I can't,' he muttered, his teeth tight.

Helen's lips shook, as realisation hit her. She closed her eyes and Paul thought the expression passing over her face was frustration. He kissed her neck, holding her close. 'I'm sorry—I'm sorry, Helen. Oh, hell, don't look like that. Tomorrow, darling, when I'm better.'

She had control of her voice now. 'You're still ill,' she said huskily. 'We should have had more sense. Of course you can't when you're running a temperature like this—don't worry, Paul.' She laughed with an effort. 'It's only temporary.'

'God, I hope so,' he said sulkily.

She smiled teasingly at him, almost lightheaded now with relief. 'I'm sure you do.'

His sullen face lightened. 'It would happen when you were saying yes for the first time in years,' he said, grinning. 'Just my luck!'

'Just mine,' Helen said with an irony he must not guess.

He laughed out loud, looking delighted. 'Did you want it badly? Poor darling!' He kissed her neck again, whispering, 'Tomorrow, Helen.'

'Yes,' she said, stroking his smooth hair. After a moment she spoke brightly. 'I'll get you some breakfast. What would you like?'

He had a boiled egg and some tea and then the need for sleep came over him again. Helen left him in the quiet room and went to ring Mark. 'Paul's ill.'

'What's wrong with him?' Mark sounded curt.

She told him and Mark said drily, 'Drunk, was he?'

She didn't answer that. 'I'm afraid neither of us will be coming in for a few days.' She paused. 'I can't leave him alone.'

There was an odd silence as though Mark heard the unspoken rider, the grim fact that she could never leave Paul, now or later. After a long moment Mark said brusquely, 'Very well. Let me know when you can start again. I'll get a temp.'

She went back to Paul later and he was awake again, irritable once more. As the days went by his improving health often made him cross and difficult. Helen bore with his moods as best as she could, grateful for the fact that Paul seemed to have forgotten any desire to make love to her. He did not ask her to sleep with him at night again, nor did he show any return of sensual interest by kissing her or caressing her. It surprised her until she thought about it and decided that Paul's male pride had been scarred by the fact that he had been unable to follow through with his earlier attempt to make love to her. He was, she suspected, waiting until he was sure he was physically back on form before he tried again. Paul would not be able to stand failing twice.

He was well enough to get up and sit watching television within a week. Helen decided she should go back to work now that he did not need constant attention, but when she announced this to Paul he scowled at her and was very difficult. 'I'll need someone around to get my meals,' he sulked.

Karen had already offered to do so, she told him without anger. Paul shrugged in petulant acceptance of this promise. The next day Helen started work again. Mark greeted her coolly, remotely. The scene between them on the moor might never have happened. Without a word spoken Mark returned to their earlier working relationship and with an aching heart Helen did so too. She had to learn to stop loving him. It sounded so easy. She had stopped loving Paul only after a painful struggle, but she knew it was going to be far harder to sop loving Mark. He was not going to make it easy for her by being cruel or cold or hurtful. Every time she looked at him she was forced to see the enduring nature of his strength and to feel a deep, reluctant ache for him which she hid beneath a cool courtesy.

She went back home that evening and the house was empty. Helen went into Karen's house and Karen looked at her with embarrassed compunction.

'He said he was bored. I think he went for a drive.'

Helen tightened. 'In his condition?' The words broke out of her and her eyes flashed.

'I did say I thought he ought to stay in today,' Karen muttered uneasily, 'but he was restless.'

'I shouldn't have left him,' Helen said aloud, biting her lip.

'Well, you couldn't stay and hold his hand for ever,' Karen pointed out. 'He seemed more or less well to me, Helen. He's a grown man and usually as fit as a flea. I shouldn't worry too much. I expect he'll be back any minute.'

Helen sat and waited with the ticking of the clock for company. Paul got back at midnight. She stood and looked at him and he shifted his feet, grimacing. 'I'm sorry, I was fed up,' he said. 'You shouldn't have left me.'

'Must I keep you on a lead for the rest of your life?' she asked tautly.

The odour of whisky clung to him and his face was tired and lined. 'Don't nag, Helen,' he muttered, turning to go up the stairs, swaying.

She helped him to his room and helped him undress, but he pushed her away with a cross, sulky gesture and got into bed, his face hidden in the pillow. His outline had a touching look, the outline of a sulking child. Helen touched his hair with a wry grimace. 'Goodnight, Paul.'

He didn't answer, and she went out without another word.

CHAPTER NINE

THERE was a staff party at the factory two days before Christmas. Helen was involved in all the final
preparations and stayed late to see them finished.
Paul had come back to work that day, but when she
saw him in the evening he told her that he would
not be home that night. 'A party at the club,' he
said, his eyes not quite meeting her own. Helen
made no comment. He was fit again and she sensed
that his need for her had fallen away once more. As
he turned away something fell from his pocket. She
picked it up and looked at the slim wrapped pack-
age. She saw the tag as she handed it back to him,
her eyes catching it without intention. Paul almost
snatched it and walked hurriedly away.

Helen had not recognised the woman's name.
Was it his current conquest? she wondered, staring
after him with a dull indifference. From the shape
and weight of the parcel she suspected it had been
jewellery. Drily she wondered if Paul had spent as
much on her Christmas present. In the past he had
always given her inexpensive gifts—underwear,
mostly, which he bought in chain stores. Paul had a
dislike of spending money where it could not get an
effect. He spent freely to establish his name as a
generous open-handed man in public, but in private he was inclined to resent every penny he was
forced to lay out.

'What are you doing for Christmas?' Mark asked

her as he walked out to the car park with her some time later.

'Spending it at home,' Helen said calmly. It was where she always spent Christmas, but she never knew whether or not she would even see Paul. Some years he went off on Christmas Eve and did not return until late on Boxing Day. He drifted like flotsam on a hospitable tide from party to party, ending up wherever he passed out, probably, and Christmas was his favourite time of year. He enjoyed the drinking, the noise, the fun which was going on around him. Helen's idea of Christmas had no meaning for him. The thought of spending it quietly with her in their home would bore Paul to tears.

Mark glanced sideways at her, his face wry. She thought he could guess at all that.

He did not make any comment, however, merely accepting what she said. 'Lift?' he asked coolly as they reached his car.

'Thank you.' She made her tones as cool as his own. He opened the door of the passenger seat and she got into it. Mark looked down at her as he closed the door again and she felt the intensity of his eyes with a painful pleasure.

He drove making small talk about the office party. When they got to her house he said goodnight without any other remark and she left him feeling as though she ached from head to foot.

The party began at lunchtime. All work stopped and everyone congregated in the large office which had been set aside the previous day. It had been hung with streamers and Christmas decorations. Holly lined the window and a couple of pieces of

mistletoe hung from the doors. Almost at once
people began to exchange teasing kisses under
them. Music blared noisily from a tape. Mark was
running the bar with cheerful efficiency. The firm
paid for half the drinks—the rest came from a float
contributed by the office staff themselves. The food
was brought by them, too; sandwiches, crisps, pea-
nuts. Helen looked after that, watching the dancing
as people began to shed their inhibitions as the
drink took an effect.

Robby Eliot came over to her and gave her an
eager smile. 'Dance with me?'

She had finished laying out the food, so she
agreed and they danced and talked for a while.
Robby told her a long and not very funny story
and she laughed obligingly. 'Oh, here's your husband,' Robby said with reluctance, glancing over
her shoulder.

Paul came up to them and Robby relinquished
her into his arms. Paul moved away, holding her
very close, his lips on her hair. 'Robby Eliot's got
his eye on you,' he said into it.

'I hadn't noticed.' She had, of course, but she had
no intention of admitting that.

'Good,' Paul said lightly. 'You belong to me, remember.'

How could she forget? she thought. Paul didn't
speak for some time and she wondered what he was
thinking, his face still on her hair, his arms holding
her tightly. They whirled round and suddenly she
saw him in a small mirror on the wall. He wasn't
aware of her at all. His bright blue eyes were fixed
on a girl from the typing pool who was sitting on a
window, her curved body provocatively posed.

Helen smiled ironically. 'I must see that the food is lasting,' she said, and Paul released her, giving her a quick smile before he turned away towards the girl he had been watching.

Helen walked away and met Mark's eyes. His face was grim and harsh in the gaudy lighting of the room. She flinched away from the blaze of his eyes and went to fuss over the half-vanished food.

She saw Paul from time to time as the party went on—he was dancing with the same girl every time, his hand fondling her as they moved. Helen looked at them with a leaden feeling of self-mockery. She saw the patterns of her life laid out in never-changing shadow. Robby came back to ask her to dance again and then she danced with several other men, but Mark did not come near her. Helen saw him dancing with others of the staff and envied them. All the girls adored him. Mark teased them, smiled at them and never stepped over the line. Helen began to ache to know what it felt like to dance with him, to feel his arms round her and his body moving against hers, but she hid her feelings under a bright smile, playing the game of enjoyment so that no one should see how miserable she really was underneath.

When Mark did come up to her she looked at him, her heart beating hard, a pulse throbbing at her throat. 'Dance?' he asked so casually, so brusquely, that she couldn't even find the words to answer. It hurt to see the contempt and coldness in his eyes.

They moved away from the group she had been with and Mark's hand tightened on her back, pressing her closer wordlessly. Being in his arms was a pleasure she could scarcely bear. She closed her eyes and Mark's cheek touched her own. Helen breathed irregularly, trembling. His hand clasped hers tighter. It was safe, she thought. They were in full view of the whole of the office and Mark had danced with everyone else. She need feel no guilt.

His thigh was moving softly against hers, his hand sliding, stroking, up and down her back. There was a restless heat growing inside her. Mark held her even tighter and she could not avoid the knowledge that his body was hard with desire. He was making private love to her right out in the middle of the room with everyone around them. Their bodies were moving urgently against each other, the surface movements of the dance only just disguising what was going on between them. Helen's face began to burn. She trembled more and more. She told herself she had to snap out of it. Forcing her eyes open, she found herself looking straight into Paul's eyes. He was pale, ashen. In the instant they looked at each other she knew he had seen the hunger for Mark burning inside her, and her colour went in a wave of white. Paul turned on his heel and went out.

Mark heard her stifled exclamation and looked down at her. 'What is it?' he asked thickly, desire still flaming in his eyes.

She halted and pushed him away, hurrying after Paul. There was no sign of him. She stood outside in the darkness, staring around her, and heard his car start with a roar. Helen ran towards it, but before she had reached it the bright streak of lights flashed away and Paul was gone.

She stood there, shivering, her arms wrapped

round her in a childish gesture of self-comfort.

Mark's steps grated behind her. He looked down at her, his eyes jealous and angry. 'At least now he knows what it feels like,' he said with harsh contempt. 'Don't look so stricken. It may do him good to realise other men want you even if he doesn't.'

'You don't understand,' she said anxiously, although she was not even sure she did, only that she had seen something in Paul's eyes that disturbed her.

'What don't I understand? That although he's a selfish swine you still love him?' Mark was talking low and bitterly. 'Or that just now you wanted me, for all that?' She flinched and he caught her arm, hurting her. 'Yes,' he said grimly, 'you did—you can't lie about that. Do you think I couldn't feel the response? Your body was mine while we danced and you know it.'

'Don't,' she said shakily.

He flung her arm down. 'I won't,' he said with his teeth tight. 'I'll keep my distance, Helen. But don't lie to me.'

She bent her head. 'Will you drive me home, please?'

'Worried in case he does something stupid?' Mark laughed with angry mockery. 'What else does he ever do? I don't need a crystal ball to predict what will happen. He'll go off and get drunk, pick up anyone who lets him and come back to you in a rotten temper tomorrow.'

Yes, she thought, that's probably how it will be, but there was still that look in Paul's eyes which bothered her as nothing about him had ever bothered her before. She could not explain it all to

Mark. It was too tenuous, too complex, for words to make it explicable to him.

'Just drive me home, please,' she said instead, quietly.

He growled something under his breath, but he walked to his car and Helen got into it. Mark drove like a bat out of hell, his face set in those harsh, jealous lines. When he stopped outside her house he said brusquely, 'Want me to come in?'

She looked at him in shock and he tightened his lips.

'In case Eastwood turns nasty,' he said, his eyes flashing a cold menace at her. 'I wasn't suggesting I stay the night, although if you offered I'd be in through the door like greased lightning.'

Helen flushed at the barbed remark. 'No, thank you,' she said.

'I thought that was what you'd say.' He was so angry he was almost shaking with it.

'I'll be all right,' she said, understanding his concern and grateful for it.

'I hope so,' Mark said shortly. 'I'll kill him if he lays so much as a hand on you.' He started the car and she got out of it. 'See you tomorrow,' he said before driving away as fast as he had come.

Paul had not come home. The house was silent and she stood there listening, trying to think. That look he had given her had shaken her. It had been a strange, fixed look which held things she was not sure she recognised. She had never seen Paul look like that before. His face had been so pale, set in such drawn lines.

She could not get to sleep. He had not come home and she hoped it was, as Mark suggested, because he had picked somebody up and got drunk. She hoped it was the usual pattern and not something new, something as disturbing as she had believed she glimpsed in him.

She finally slept in the early hours of the morning. When she got up the next day Paul still had not come home. She got ready for work, puzzled and disturbed, and when she got there she slipped down to his office, but there was no sign of him there either.

He did not come into work at all that day. Mark made no comment, but his eyes watched Helen closely as she was getting ready to go. 'Have a good Christmas,' he said, and she politely returned the greeting.

Mark caught her arm as she turned to go. 'Helen, come to us for Christmas,' he said huskily.

She felt a sweetness rise inside her and smiled at him with the love she could not suppress. 'Thank you, but I can't.'

His eyes narrowed on her face, suddenly very bright and hard, and she was afraid of what he might have seen in her eyes. When he spoke, however, he gave no indication that he had glimpsed her feelings.

'What if Eastwood doesn't turn up all over Christmas? Are you going to sing a lonely carol round your Christmas tree and eat one mince pie?'

She forced a brief laughter. 'I'll be fine. Paul will come home.'

'Will he?' Mark's mouth moved derisively. 'Shall we lay odds, Helen?'

She shook her head, looking away.

'I won't have you sitting at home on your own

all over Christmas,' Mark said forcefully, his hand
tightening round her arm.

'I have to be there,' she said, trying to explain.

'In case he does come?'

She nodded.

'You fool, Helen,' Mark ground out thickly. 'You
silly obstinate little fool!' His head bent and he
glared at her, eyes dark. 'Are you going to spend the
rest of your life sitting waiting for him?'

'Probably,' she said with wry self-understanding.

Mark swore.

He drove her home and left her with a curt word.
Helen felt tears rising to her eyes as she went into
the house. She hated Mark's anger; it hurt her.
How could she tell him that she had to be at home
in case Paul needed her? Mark would misunder-
stand. He would read it for undying love when it
was something else, something so complicated she
did not understand it herself, only that she could
not turn her back on Paul's weakness and insuffi-
ciency.

That was what had disturbed her when she realised he had seen and recognised her feelings for
Mark. Paul had looked stricken, lost, a child whose
mother had wandered away from it. If she left Paul
she did not need to guess how he would end up—
his hollow incapacity for love would make of any
relationship he formed a brief, doomed spell. Paul
would slide and slide until he was trapped in a hell
of loneliness. Helen's last remnant of love for him,
her fondness which was born of understanding and
past shared love, made her unable to walk away
from anything so helpless and weak.

She could not even guess how Paul would react

now that he knew for certain that she loved Mark.

He did not come home, however, and in the end she went to bed; all the gaudy trappings of Christmas making the house a glittering sham. The silence around her was emphasised by her awareness of the joy and pleasure which would be in other homes tonight. She had heard Terry's excited squealing as she went up to bed to struggle for sleep with all the glorious excitement of Christmas morning in prospect. Karen and her husband had come in for a drink, making no comment on Paul's absence, their faces tactful, sympathetic, faintly embarrassed. Karen awkwardly muttered an invitation for Helen to join them for Christmas Day. 'Bring Paul, of course,' she said quickly, trying to sound as though she expected Paul to be around. Helen thanked her but refused. 'Paul likes a quiet Christmas,' she lied, and they reluctantly smiled back at her, hiding their realisation that she lied.

Waking on a bright Christmas morning, Helen listened and heard no sound from Paul's room. She went in and the bed was untouched, empty. She made herself a slice of toast and prepared the Christmas lunch she had bought. She was going through the motions like a robot, but she was beginning to be sure he would not come home.

The day ticked on slowly. She heard laughter and music from Karen's house and deliberately kept her television on quite loudly to make it sound as though the house were not empty and null.

She was grateful for their tact in not coming in to make sure; that would have been too embarrassing to bear.

It was after six that somebody knocked on the

door. Helen stared at it, standing in the hall, shivering. It could be Karen having decided to risk asking her round there again, or it could be someone to tell her Paul had crashed his car again. She knew as she thought it that that had been in her mind all day, the fear that something had happened to him. The knock came again, louder, peremptory. It had an official sound, a determined, authoritative sound.

Helen tremblingly opened the door.

Before she could move to stop him Mark had pushed his way into the house. They faced each other almost like enemies. His eyes were hard and glittered.

'He isn't here, is he?'

'What are you doing here?' Helen asked, ignoring the question. 'Please just leave me alone.'

'Get your coat.'

'No, Mark,' she said angrily.

He took a loping stride and she backed until she was against the wall. Mark kissed her mouth savagely, demandingly, holding her there, his hands coming down after a moment to touch her breasts in a deliberate motion which was a silent challenge to her to deny him now. All the fight went out of her slowly and she began to moan softly, the hard desire of his body pressed against her.

'Say it,' Mark muttered.

For one last anguished moment she tried to hold the words back, but they came out at last on a hoarse, tired whisper. 'I love you.'

His arms went round her and he held her cradled like a child, kissing her hair with a hungry passion which held relief and joy.

'My darling, oh, my darling,' he whispered.

She closed her eyes and let the whole weight of her body lean on him with a gesture of contented love. For a moment nothing else mattered but the love encircling them like the rainbow rings around the moon on winter nights, a misty radiance like spilt petrol, pale and flaming, magical.

Mark lifted his head at last. 'Get your coat,' he said again.

'Mark, I can't!'

'You can and you will,' he said decisively. 'You are not spending a lonely vigil round a Christmas tree if I can stop it. I've spoken to my mother and she understands.'

'Does she?' Helen could not hide the disbelief, the doubt in her voice.

Mark looked down at her with a wry twist of the mouth. 'I won't say she's delighted at the prospect of some scandal touching the family, but I've told her I love you and I've told her what you've put up with from Eastwood. She won't be unkind to you, my darling, I promise that. My mother is a strong woman, but she isn't a cold or a cruel one. She'll love you when she gets to know you. There's a lot in common between you. I think you'll find you like her when you know her well.'

'I'm sure I would,' Helen said dully. 'But it isn't just that, Mark. It ...' She broke off, not knowing how to say it.

'It's what?' he asked keenly, watching her. 'Still Eastwood? Are you afraid of what he may do?'

She nodded and he moved restlessly.

'Helen, the probability is that he won't come home all Christmas. I know that, you know that.

On top of that, why should he expect you to sit around and wait for him alone for days while he enjoys himself with other women?'

She smiled drily. 'Paul doesn't think like that. He doesn't think at all. All Paul knows is that I should be here when he wants me.'

Mark's eyes flashed. 'And you put up with that?'

'What else can I do?'

He stared at her and his eyes were bitter. 'You love me, but you're prepared to let him go on stamping all over you? Why?'

Helen made an attempt to explain, her voice low and unsteady. 'He's a child, Mark. If I walk out on him what will happen to him?'

'Who cares?' Mark had the irritated impatience of a man who has stood enough. 'You're coming with me, Helen, and you're going to enjoy Christmas as it was meant to be enjoyed, among a loving family.' He paused. 'Or do I have to take you upstairs and make you do as I say?'

Her face burst into burning colour.

Mark eyed her ironically. 'I could, couldn't I? You showed me that just now. I felt it when we danced at the office party. Whatever you were saying to me, your body was talking another language, and when I realised that it gave me a new hope. I can't talk sense into you, but now I know I've got another method of communicating which works.'

Helen couldn't look at him, trembling.

'So get your coat,' he said gently, 'or upstairs we go.'

He spoke so softly, yet there was an expression in his eyes which held warning. Helen did not quite dare to challenge him. Mark was right: they were talking calmly to each other, but under that their bodies were in permanent dialogue of a different kind and Helen could not deny the fact that urgency was growing in her as it was in Mark. It would be safer to do as he said.

It was so long since she had spent a happy family Christmas without a shadow over it. As Mark drove her towards his house she stared at it, wondering what sort of reception she would get this time from his mother.

'Jo's home,' Mark told her as he swerved up the drive.

That news made Helen even more nervous and Mark shot her a brief, understanding look. 'She's fine,' he said, and the laconic little phrase eased Helen's frown.

'You think she's over him?'

He grinned. 'I suspect so, from the way she's been talking non-stop about a certain six-foot rugger player she's met.'

Helen laughed. 'That sounds ominous!'

'Doesn't it just? I don't know that I'm up to tackling a twenty-year-old with shoulders like barn walls. She's got a photo of him and I'm not exaggerating. He looks as if he grew up wrestling with polar bears for fun.'

Helen relaxed beside him, her eyes full of amusement. She was still smiling as Mark guided her to the front door. It opened and with a dying smile she faced his mother, her hands going cold, trembling. Mark took one of them firmly.

There was a brief, tense silence. Helen held her head up, her eyes meeting Mrs Eliot's and her facial muscles rigorously controlled. Mrs Eliot looked probingly into her face for a moment and then she smiled quite gently. 'Happy Christmas, Helen. I'm glad Mark persuaded you to join us.'

Helen slackened, trembling, all her nervous tension relaxing again, and managed to say: 'Thank you for inviting me.'

'You may regret it,' Mrs Eliot said with a dry amusement. 'I'm afraid the house is full to overflowing with people who seem to think that noise is a necessary part of Christmas.'

'Well, isn't it?' Mark asked, grinning. 'She loves it, Helen. Don't let her regal manner fool you.'

From the drawing-room Helen had already caught the wild gales of laughter, barking from the dogs, a muffled crack as someone pulled a Christmas cracker and the dogs all barked again. 'Come and say hello,' Mark told her. 'At Christmas if you can't beat them you join them.'

The room was crammed with people at first glance. They all looked round, their faces filled with enjoyment and laughter. Helen recognised most of them. Mark waved a hand. 'You haven't met my sister Anne, have you? Anne, Frank—this is Helen.'

In a quick glance Helen absorbed Anne's short dark curls, her calmly vague expression, her pleasant smile. She was a fainter version of the Eliot looks, her blue eyes pale, her manner less expressive. Her husband was a short, partly balding man with quiet dark eyes. Helen smiled at them both and got back friendly smiles in return.

Patsy jumped up and caught Helen's hands, tugging at her. 'Come and play. We're racing matchboxes!'

Robby was sprawling full length on the carpet, grinning. 'Patsy's idea,' he disclaimed.

'Go on, you're loving it,' said Joanne, poking him in the back. She gave Helen a quick, over-bright smile as she spoke, but there was none of the hostility in her eyes that Helen had seen there before.

'How do you play?' Helen asked, and Patsy burst into confused explanations which Robby helped out with a demonstration, carefully guiding a matchbox along the floor with his nose.

'You can be in my team,' Joanne said.

'No, she's in mine,' Patsy at once challenged.

'*I'm* in yours,' said Mark, kneeling down and getting a broad grin from his delighted niece.

'Come on, Nanna,' Patsy begged. 'Don't just stand there and watch. Everyone has to play, even Buster.'

'Not Buster,' Joanne argued. 'You know what will happen.'

'Buster loves playing games!'

'Yes, but he makes such a racket,' Joanne protested, eyeing him with disfavour.

Buster, seeing himself to be the centre of attention and loving it, licked her vigorously and she shoved him away. He fell over Mark and they rolled across the room, Buster barking wildly, Mark groaning as the huge hairy body bounced all over him.

'Get him off me, Patsy! That animal can cause more damage than a ten-ton truck!'

Helen watched Mark with unguarded passion and love, all that he was revealed in his casual, loving treatment of both his niece and the dog; firmness allied to tenderness, that strength of his never used to harm or hurt anyone.

She looked up, realising she was being watched herself, and met his mother's eyes. Helen felt her cheeks glow with pink and was about to look away when Mrs Eliot smiled at her. Helen smiled back, tentatively, shyly.

In that instant she felt Mrs Eliot's acceptance of the situation and was so moved by it that she felt tears prick at her eyes and had to look away to hide them.

She had dreaded what she would find when she met Mark's mother again, and now her fears vanished.

From that moment the evening took on an enchanted glow. Helen joined in the games which Patsy insisted on organising, sang carols with them and watched a film on television. Mark sprawled on the carpet at her feet, his dark head against her knees. His family seemed aware of it, yet Helen felt no hostility among them. She sensed that some sort of family discussion had already taken place, that Mark had made his intentions clear and that if there had been any disapproval it had been talked out. She got no angry vibrations. Everyone was friendly, smiling, welcoming.

Helen helped Mrs Eliot and Anne serve the evening meal, which was a high tea in the Northern tradition: cold pork and turkey, pickles, salad, trifle and jelly, Christmas cake and mince pies.

The Eliots were an extrovert family, cheerfully rude to each other, shouting each other down in argument, laughing and enjoying every moment of the occasion. Mark listened and put in a word, grinning. When Patsy and Robby broke into real quarrelling he stopped it with a crisp word, his face firm but not angry, and they lapsed obediently.

Helen saw Patsy discreetly slipping titbits from her plate to Buster, whose bulk was hidden under the table. Catching Helen's amused eye, Patsy winked at her shamelessly.

As Helen looked away, smiling, she caught Mark's eyes on her and he grinned too, telling her that he knew very well Buster was under there but was ignoring it for the moment.

When the film followed the meal, Patsy sat on the floor with her arms round her knees, watching intently while her dog slumbered at her side, making the occasional comment, pleased when everyone laughed.

The age differences in the room seemed of little importance. They all treated each other on the same level as though Patsy's words held as much weight as Mrs Eliot's; a loving courtesy which Helen found very impressive. They teased each other, mocked each other, argued with each other and were never malicious or unpleasant. Watching them, Helen saw that the shaping hand in this family pattern was that of Mrs Eliot. She was interested in everyone, everything; open-minded in a confident assertive fashion and prepared to take Patsy as seriously as Patsy took herself. Such adult treatment had to be responsible for the easy, happy confidence which Patsy made apparent in everything she said.

'Who would like cocoa?' Mrs Eliot asked as the film ended, and got back a chorus of agreement. She looked at Helen. 'Come and help me, Helen.'

Helen followed her into the kitchen and arranged a row of mugs while Mrs Eliot put milk on to heat. While they worked, Mrs Eliot began to ask Helen questions casually—not about Paul, but about her family, her childhood, listening interestedly as Helen answered.

Just before they carried the mugs of cocoa back to the others, the older woman said quietly: 'I'd begun to think Mark would never marry. It's made me sad that he didn't seem able to find anyone he wanted enough. If you can make him happy, Helen, I shall welcome you with open arms.'

Helen's throat closed. 'Thank you,' she said drily, meeting the direct blue eyes.

'Mark has explained it all,' Mrs Eliot went on flatly. 'What are you going to do?'

Helen looked away and knew with a certainty she had never felt before. 'I shall go away to London and divorce my husband.'

'You're going away?' Mrs Eliot looked surprised. 'Mark didn't tell me that.'

'He doesn't know—I haven't told him yet. But I think I must. I must have a breathing space; we both must. It will take time for me to get a divorce and it wouldn't be fair to Mark for me to stay here while I do it.'

There was a little silence, then Mrs Eliot said firmly: 'I think you're very wise. Mark will argue with you. Don't let him talk you out of it. If you're to be happy together you have to start in the right way.'

Helen nodded. 'Yes, I know.'

When they went back into the crowded, noisy room Helen felt Mark watching her and knew that he had guessed his mother was seizing a chance to talk to her privately. She avoided his eyes because she felt sad whenever she faced the prospect of going away and leaving him. It had to be done, but it would not be easy.

She stayed the night at the house, sharing a room with Patsy and, she discovered in the morning, Buster too, since at some time in the night Patsy must have got up to admit him. Wickedly Patsy grinned at her as Helen eyed the dog. 'Don't tell Mark!'

Breakfast was something of a scratch meal since only half the party got up for it. It was a crisp, clear day. Frost rimed the fields and sparkled on the trees and roofs. Mark was up when Helen went downstairs and after breakfast he persuaded her and Patsy to walk with him across the brown moors. The dogs came, leaping and racing along in front, and Patsy ran with them, her energy restored to a vital level.

'What were you talking to my mother about last night?' Mark asked as they walked.

Patsy was out of earshot, so Helen quietly told him and Mark gave her a quick, unsmiling look. 'You're not going away,' he said in a curt voice. 'No, Helen.'

'I have to, Mark. How could I stay in Ryethorpe while I was divorcing Paul?'

Mark's face hardened. 'He'll have to go, of course. I'll find him another job elsewhere.'

She winced. Paul would blame her for that. Mark caught her expression and sighed. 'I know, it's difficult. But he'd make trouble if he was around here and I want him right out of our lives.'

Helen walked on, shivering.

'I won't let you go,' Mark said tautly at her side, his hand catching at her elbow to halt her. 'If I let you out of my sight, Eastwood would try to talk you back to him.' The blue eyes had a deep angry glow. 'You're still half committed to him. Do you think I'm not aware of that?'

'How can I help it? Whatever he's done, there's still so much behind us.'

'It's water under a bridge, Helen. Face it—your marriage has been dead for years. You've dragged it around like a decaying corpse and it's poisoning your life.' His voice whipped like a lash, savage and cold. 'The swine isn't getting away with it for ever—I won't let him!'

Last night in the middle of his warm, happy family with laughter and love all round her it had all looked so simple for a while. Helen had seen how life could be for her and had realised how little reality her marriage held. She had already committed the betrayal of Paul which love for another man implied—Paul knew that now. He knew her too well not to have realised that the desire she had been unable to hide must have love behind it. Helen had never showed signs of attraction to anyone before. Paul had instinctively recognised the drag of awareness between Helen and Mark right at the start; the dog-in-the-manger spite he had shown whenever he spoke of Mark had warned Helen of that. Paul would not easily let her go, but if she stayed she would never get anything back from him. Paul was incapable of adult love. The stricken pallor of his face as he realised how deeply she wanted Mark had not been the jealousy of a man who loves a woman, it had been the shock of a child when it first discovers that its mother is capable of other, wider loyalties. Paul had suddenly seen his possession of her slipping from him, and that was what had made his eyes glitter so savagely.

She shivered. Paul's anger could be dangerous. He had that streak of spiteful sadism, a pleasure got from hurting, and whenever his desire was thwarted it came out. Helen had been afraid ever since the office party, although she could not guess at what Paul would do, only that he would look for some way to hurt both her and Mark.

Mark was watching her intently and as she looked up and their eyes met he said quickly, 'Don't go back to that house, Helen.'

A silent understanding passed between them in her caught breath. Mark too suspected that Paul would want vengeance. Did he guess what form that revenge would take? Helen felt sickness in the back of her throat. She did. Paul, if he got the chance, would use a weapon he had tried to use before—he would regard it as apt and amusing to force her to give him what he would now know she would find intolerable.

Mark had whitened as he watched her. 'I'd kill him if he touched you,' he muttered under his breath, his voice shaking.

Mark's ability to read her thoughts no longer surprised her. He had shown her again and again that he could understand her without words.

Patsy was racing ahead with the dogs still, her laughter audible above their excited barking. Mark shot a look after her and grinned. 'That child is crammed with energy. Where on earth does she get it? Just watching her makes me feel tired!'

Helen sensed that he was trying to relieve the tension between them, return them to a more even level of emotion. She smiled at him to reassure him.

'She's a darling and I love her. I love all your family.'

'I'm glad about that,' Mark retorted, grinning. 'I'd hate to have to kill them all off.'

Helen laughed, eyes bright. 'I don't want you to lose anything, Mark. I'd hate to feel I've harmed you in any way.' Although she spoke lightly her words were serious and he took them as such.

'You haven't and you won't, darling. I've been waiting for you all my life. I always knew that somewhere there was a girl with green eyes and a mane of silvery hair.' His eyes teased her. 'But you took your time in showing up.'

Patsy had fallen in her headlong chase and the dogs seethed around her, encouraging her to get up with barks and wet kisses. 'Get off, you mangy hounds!' Patsy bellowed loudly, and Helen and Mark stood watching, laughing. Patsy's exuberant amusement spread to them and Helen felt suddenly five years younger, the weight of her life with Paul shed from her shoulders, gaiety and happiness in her smile.

She had not felt as free and alive in years. Mark looked down at her laughing face and his eyes grew passionate. His hand groped for hers and held it, swinging between them, a physical link which completed the circle of their love.

Over the heather-thick brow of the hill came a row of horses, galloping gingerly over the frosty ground. 'Boxing Day fun and games,' Mark commented, glancing briefly at their dark outlines. 'The country club fraternity, I expect. They usually ride out this way.

'Patsy, we'll turn back!' he shouted towards his niece, who got up with the dogs bounding around her and turned back towards them. Helen stood watching the riders as they wheeled away towards the distant road. Suddenly one of them peeled off and came towards her, and with a leap of the heart she recognised Paul in white sweater and jeans. His face was set in a vicious white mask. Even at a distance she could read the rage in his face.

Mark had not noticed him. He turned to Helen and put a casual arm around her shoulders; possessive, loving but without sensuality. She looked up at him, but before she could speak and warn him of Paul's approach Patsy yelled: 'Stop Buster, Mark! He's after rabbits again!'

Buster was lolloping along with his tongue out and an excited expression. Mark, grinning, broke away from Helen and headed him off, whistling.

Paul's course swerved in answer to Mark's movements and suddenly Helen saw what he meant to do.

'Mark!' she screamed.

At her panic-stricken voice Mark swung, stiffening, and saw Paul thundering down on him. Helen began to run towards him, her heart pounding inside her. Paul was going to ride Mark down: she had seen it in a flash. His teeth were bared in a savage grin and his features stripped to their basic element of self-indulgent spite. Helen knew the way Paul's mind worked. Seeing them laughing together, happy together, he had been furious and in an instant he had made up his mind to smash what they had like a thwarted child who will break another child's toy merely because he wants it and cannot have it. Paul was taking a gamble, but he would have believed in his own ability to lie convincingly. If he had caught Mark unaware he would have said his horse had run away with him, pretended shock and horror, even wept in mock distress.

'Get back, Helen!' Mark shouted as she came towards him, and the crack of his voice stopped her in her tracks.

The horse was galloping flat out, unstoppable, the reins pulled right back and the head up, nostrils flaring, teeth clamped.

Mark faced it calmly, his lean body poised. A second before the horse would hit him he leapt aside with a balletic spring and it sailed harmlessly on. Helen ran to Mark and flung herself against him, holding him in her arms, her cheek against his sweater, hearing his living heart beat on under her wet face. The tears ran down her cheeks. What might have happened had shown her at last what she would be losing if she did not choose Mark now and for ever. She would have wanted to die if Mark had gone down under Paul's hooves.

Patsy had stopped dead, staring in shocked amazement. 'If he'd hurt you—' Helen groaned out, and Mark kissed her hair.

'I'm safe, darling,' he muttered. 'Stop trembling, Helen—I'm safe.' His words broke off and she felt his body stiffen. He thrust her back from him with a rough gesture. 'Get out of the way, Helen!'

She turned and saw Paul riding back towards

them at the same furious pace. Buster was barking, his great head lifted as he watched the curious antics going on around him. Patsy had his collar, but as she realised Paul was coming back her hand must have slipped. Buster broke from her grip, eager to join in whatever game was happening, tearing towards Paul's horse and giving out a deep bell-like clamour.

'Buster!' Patsy shrieked.

Mark's head swung and took in what was happening. 'Buster,' he ordered harshly, 'back!'

The large shambling bulk braked obediently, still barking, and turned to go back to Patsy with a grudging look at Mark for being such a spoilsport.

Paul's horse shied, the dog's barking and white blur of movement alarming it. It skidded sideways, its impetus taking it over on to its side at full speed, and Helen screamed as Paul sailed over its head.

The horse scrambled up, unharmed apparently, and moved away, trembling, breathing hard, flanks heaving and sweat pouring down the silken coat.

Helen and Mark moved at the same time. Helen fell to her knees beside Paul's still figure. Mark slowly, carefully turned him on to his back, his arms limp at his sides. There was blood smeared across the golden hair, and Helen caught her breath. She watched tensely as Mark's long fingers felt for Paul's pulse.

Patsy slowly came up and stood behind them, watching. The dogs sat, panting, at her feet, interested observers.

'Is he badly hurt?' Helen watched Mark's set face anxiously. 'Mark, is it serious?'

Paul was not moving. She watched the straight

line of his lips and tried to catch the note of his breathing.

Mark knelt looking at her, not speaking, his face haggard.

'Mark?' Helen's body froze in icy disbelief at something in his eyes.

Mark's eyes slid aside and she saw him looking at the rusty dark heather. Among them a jagged rock thrust up. Helen suddenly saw the bright streak of blood it carried and her heart stopped.

'He must have hit his head as he fell,' Mark said harshly. 'At that speed, wearing no hat, he wouldn't have had a chance.'

Helen looked down at Paul, her ears hearing nothing more. She put out a shaking hand to stroke back the smooth golden hair from his damp forehead. He lay so still and tranquil in the cold wintry light, all the glitter of sunlight in his hair as it gleamed. His face had smoothed out into beauty again, as it did when he slept. Paul was beautiful, Helen thought, gazing down at him. He would always be beautiful now. The slow stain which had begun to eat up that beauty had been halted for ever. All that Paul could have been lay in that peaceful face. The ruin of his life was now behind him. Helen put her hands over her face and wept.

Here is a selection of Mills & Boon novels to be
published at about the same time as the book you
are reading.

PACT WITHOUT DESIRE	*Jane Arbor*
MOONLIGHT ON THE NILE	*Elizabeth Ashton*
THE MAN ON THE PEAK	*Katrina Britt*
THE VITAL SPARK	*Angela Carson*
RETURN TO DEVIL'S VIEW	*Rosemary Carter*
MY LOVE GOES WITH YOU	*Lilian Chisholm*
THE LION'S DEN	*Ann Cooper*
THE SPANISH UNCLE	*Jane Corrie*
SOLITAIRE	*Sara Craven*
FOR MIKE'S SAKE	*Janet Dailey*
A LAND CALLED DESERET	*Janet Dailey*
SENTIMENTAL JOURNEY	*Janet Dailey*
THAT BOSTON MAN	*Janet Dailey*
THE ANGRY MAN	*Joyce Dingwell*
SHADOW OF THE PAST	*Robyn Donald*
A SAVAGE SANCTUARY	*Jane Donnelly*
DARK ENCOUNTER	*Susanna Firth*
PICTURE OF JULIE	*Kate Garrick*
HEPBURN'S QUAY	*Lucy Gillen*
COME NEXT SPRING	*Elizabeth Graham*
HEART OF THE SCORPION	*Janice Gray*
CHATEAU IN THE PALMS	*Anne Hampson*
A ROSE FROM LUCIFER	*Anne Hamspon*
TANGLED SHADOWS	*Flora Kidd*
TOGETHER AGAIN	*Flora Kidd*
DARK DOMINION	*Charlotte Lamb*
LOVE IS A FRENZY	*Charlotte Lamb*
POSSESSION	*Charlotte Lamb*
TWIST OF FATE	*Charlotte Lamb*
THE TIDES OF LOVE	*Marguerite Lees*

MY SISTER'S KEEPER	*Rachel Lindsay*
EARLY SUMMER	*Jan MacLean*
TWO FOR JOY	*Audrie Manley-Tucker*
THE JUDAS TRAP	*Anne Mather*
LURE OF EAGLES	*Anne Mather*
ISLAND OF CYCLONES	*Wynne May*
MISTAKEN MARRIAGE	*Margaret Mayo*
MAN OF THE HIGH COUNTRY	*Mary Moore*
THE TEMPESTUOUS FLAME	*Carole Mortimer*
TEMPTED BY DESIRE	*Carole Mortimer*
MIDNIGHT SUN'S MAGIC	*Betty Neels*
THE PROMISE OF HAPPINESS	*Betty Neels*
THE DEVIL'S BRIDE	*Margaret Pargeter*
SAVAGE POSSESSION	*Margaret Pargeter*
ENEMY FROM THE PAST	*Lilian Peake*
WHITE HIBISCUS	*Rosemary Pollock*
CASTLE OF THE FOUNTAINS	*Margaret Rome*
MIX ME A MAN	*Doris E. Smith*
HOSTILE ENGAGEMENT	*Jessica Steele*
INTIMATE ENEMIES	*Jessica Steele*
CLOSE TO THE HEART	*Rebecca Stratton*
ONE MORE RIVER TO CROSS	*Essie Summers*
THIS SIDE OF PARADISE	*Kay Thorpe*
STOWAWAY	*Anne Weale*
THE ICE MAIDEN	*Sally Wentworth*
BITTER ENCHANTMENT	*Yvonne Whittal*
RUNAWAY MARRIAGE	*Mary Wibberley*
WITH THIS RING	*Mary Wibberley*
THE SHEIK'S CAPTIVE	*Violet Winspear*

£3.25 net each